Time to Change

Usefull intro to some of the main issues but not hugely practical on what 2 do + theological aspects bit limited

TIME TO CHANGE

Challenge for an endangered planet

Hugh Montefiore

Published by
The Bible Reading Fellowship
Peter's Way, Sandy Lane West
Oxford OX4 5HG
ISBN 0 7459 2526 X
Albatross Books Pty Ltd
PO Box 320, Sutherland
NSW 2232, Australia
ISBN 0 7324 1562 4

First edition 1997
10 9 8 7 6 5 4 3 2 1 0

Acknowledgments
Unless otherwise stated, scripture quotations are
taken from the Revised Standard Version of the
Bible (RSV) copyright © 1946, 1952, 1971 by the
Division of Christian Education of the National
Council of the Churches of Christ in the USA.

A catalogue record for this book is
available from the British Library

Printed and bound in Great Britain
by Cox and Wyman Limited, Reading

Contents

[illegible]

Foreword

When the world began to realize the serious nature of the environmental crisis which we face, few Christians took any notice. One most conspicuous exception was the Bishop of Birmingham, Hugh Montefiore, who began to express environmental concern long before it was fashionable. For some time he was a lone voice prophesying in the wilderness. Today some parts of the Church are slowly beginning to realize that the Church has a special role in the care of God's creation, but, as the last chapter of this book shows, like the first-century church in Laodicea, the attitude is still lukewarm. As the title of this book implies, it is time for Christians to wake up to their responsibility, it is time to change.

As an environmental scientist I am particularly impressed that here we not only have authoritative interpretation of the scriptures, but also an excellent scientific exposition of the environmental crisis. The carefully selected topics of each chapter contain a great deal of scientific facts which demonstrate that the earth is facing a major crisis. These are topics, based on sound science, which we all need to heed and to take seriously. Throughout the book there are many suggestions for action. This is not a book to read and put aside but one on which first to meditate and then act. As the author points out the Bible is not an environmental textbook and there are not scriptures directly concerned with the topics of all chapters. However, I found that each of the scriptures chosen is relevant and thought provoking; each chapter requires thoughtful meditation and prayer. The science and the scriptures have been carefully blended and I sincerely hope that this book will help to awaken concern for creation amongst Christians who should be the first people ready to act to stop the destruction of God's good creation. I share Hugh Montefiore's conviction that church people should be in the front line of the battle to save the environment and perhaps even the existence of life on earth. It is indeed a time for the Church to change, and here we have an excellent summary of the many reasons why, put into a biblical and devotional context. May we all as Christians read, pray and act to save our fragile planet.

Professor Sir Ghillean Prance, FRS

Preface

This book about the environment has been written in order to stir people to commitment and action in helping to save it. There was, of course, no environmental crisis when the books of the Bible were originally written, but the moral and spiritual message of the Bible readings in each section are as applicable now to the environment as they were to the situations to which they were first addressed. The stories describe the human condition, its possibilities and glories as well as its flaws and selfishness. The latter are the cause of so many of our environmental problems. Each section ends with a prayer or passage for reflection. I am grateful to Shelagh Brown for her assistance with these, and for her encouragement over the book as a whole.

It is hard to realize that humanity is probably facing the greatest crisis in its history, and that unless we take more resolute action that crisis will turn into a catastrophe. I write in the passionate conviction that church people should be foremost in the battle to save the environment, for the world is part of God's gift to us to care for and not to abuse. Alas, in the last quarter century since we first became aware of the perils that we face through our treatment of the environment, the Church has not played a leading part: indeed it has scarcely played any part at all. This must change. Not only is it urgent to move the hearts of all to respect the environment, but also church people need to know the basic facts about how we are endangering it. Otherwise, how can we change our ways?

It is my hope and prayer that these notes may contribute to these goals.

+*Hugh Montefiore*

1

Good news for the whole world

Jesus did not preach about acid rain or global warming or the ozone layer or other environmental issues. He preached about the kingdom of God and our relationship to it. If he did not worry about such things, why should we?

There were no global problems of the environment in his day. It is only lately, since the technological revolution and the vast expansion of human population and activity, that such problems have arisen. So, in a sense, there was nothing to preach about on these issues. Jesus preached salvation, and that meant saving us from the effects of our folly and sins, and saving us for our eternal destiny to be with God for ever. His preaching was not simply about our preparation for this future destiny. It was also about the here and now. The kingdom of God means the rule or reign of God over the whole earth. It will never be complete on this earth until God brings his purpose to an end: as Paul wrote, 'Flesh and blood cannot inherit the kingdom of God' (1 Corinthians 15:50). But we can catch glimpses of it in this world. Jesus himself inaugurated it by his coming, because that put people in a new relationship with God, so that they could better acknowledge his kingship.

Jesus did not describe what the kingdom of God is like. Of course not: how can one describe God's rule over everybody and everything? That is what the kingdom of God means: where God is not only supreme, but acknowledged as supreme. What Jesus did do was to show us aspects of what the kingdom of God is like. He did this by parables: it is like the seed growing secretly, it is like a dragnet, it is like a grain of mustard seed, like leaven, like a lost coin, and so on. In this way he gave an imaginative insight into the effect that the kingdom of God has on us, or the attitudes that are needed in order to enter into the kingdom of God.

If God is supreme over everybody and everything, that must mean that he is not only supreme in the hearts of men and women, but also over the whole of society in which we live. Jesus himself is not the Christ because he talked about the kingdom, but because he himself was the bearer of the kingdom: he brought it by his own presence. Wherever we are, he makes us aware of the heavenly rule of our heavenly Father. Through him we are brought face to face with God himself. He embodied in his person the kingdom of God because he was perfectly obedient to his heavenly Father. He spoke of the kingdom drawing near, as if it were just round the corner during his lifetime, casting its shadow before it came more fully with his death and resurrection. He spoke in this anticipatory way because it was not until his death and resurrection that Jesus completed the task of bringing the kingdom and enabling us to share it with him. In this way he brought us salvation.

The rule of God should be manifested in the attitudes and behaviour of individuals and of society. But the rule of God extends over the whole world, and that must include the natural world. Here there are many glimpses of God's rule for those who have eyes to see. One of the ways in which God exercises this rule is by his providential ordering of the world. When it is realized how many contingencies there are in the evolution of the universe, the Milky Way, the sun and its planets, the infinite wisdom of God becomes evident. The sun is kept at the right temperature, comfortable for life. There are wonderful systems of recycling trace minerals necessary for life. The sea is kept at the right saline mixture. The air cleanses itself naturally, and oxygen is renewed by a complex system by which chlorophyll in green things enables plants to absorb carbon and to transpire oxygen. Water is recycled by evaporation from the oceans into the skies, and falls again as rain upon the earth. We have food to eat, water to drink, and shelter and clothes with which to protect ourselves. The list of God's providential care goes on and on. For those who have eyes to see, this is all part of his kingly rule. From others it is hidden, because they only look on it as the way in which things naturally happen in accordance with the mechanisms and laws which the natural sciences have uncovered.

To interfere with these natural processes is to interfere with the kingly rule of God. It is to substitute the selfish dominion of mankind for the rule of God. Jesus preached: 'Repent, for the kingdom of heaven is at hand'. The world should repent (amongst other things) of the present harm that it is doing to the environment, and mend its ways. The word used here in the Greek for repentance (*metanoeite*) means a change of heart. Christ called for a change of heart which involves putting God first instead of our own selfish interests. Without this it is not really possible to believe in the good news of the gospel.

That call of Jesus applies to our whole attitude to life: it certainly applies to the way in which we treat our environment. We are told in the scriptures that God gave to mankind dominion over the earth; and this is a fact. Mankind is indeed dominant over the environment in which we live. But God also made all mankind in his own image, and that means that we must exercise our dominion responsibly and in a godlike way. We must work with the grain of God's kingly rule over the environment. God has built into creation what we may call the natural law, which enables the planet to be kept comfortable for life. Our selfish and sinful domination of the world will lead to destruction and disaster. But to cooperate with God's kingly rule in creation will lead to restoration, and enable the planet to remain comfortable for life, and thereby enable it to carry out God's purposes.

All human beings are made in God's image, however badly we may mar that image. It follows therefore that one aspect of the kingdom of God is to recognize that every human being is equally a member of the human family. We are all sons and daughters of God because God is the Father of all, in whose image we all are made. So human beings in society should work together and the nations of the world should cooperate in measures which enable God's kingly rule to be substituted for the selfish dominion of man over the proper functioning of the environment.

Through the providence of God mankind has developed intelligence, and we must use that intelligence creatively, in adapting the world of nature without endangering it. For example, we could use advanced technology to make the seeds which we sow pest-resistant and disease-resistant. In that kind of creative activity, we would be following in the footsteps of God the Creator. We must try to put right those aspects of the environment which others before us (and perhaps we ourselves) have spoilt. That would indeed be helping to redeem the world, and we would be following in the steps of God, our Redeemer. We must also recognize the intrinsic worth of all creation, and the part that it plays in making the world comfortable for life: the rocks, the trees, the air, bacteria, micro-organisms, all living things great and small. That would be our way of sanctifying creation. We would be following in the footsteps of God the Sanctifier, for God's Holy Spirit sanctifies all creation. We are to be co-creators, co-redeemers, co-sanctifiers with God. That does not mean that mankind is anywhere near the same level as God, but that mankind will be living as people made in God's image, and therefore following in his footsteps.

It follows from this that to assert God's kingly rule over the whole environment, and to repent of our interference with that rule, is as necessary as to assert God's kingly rule over our personal lives and over the life of society. It therefore is a duty laid upon all Christians to care for the environment in which they live. This applies at a global level, and it applies also at a personal level. Human interference can scar the natural beauty of the countryside as well as interfere with the natural ecosystems which keep the world comfortable for life. Our task in a decade of evangelism is to prepare for the coming of God's kingdom more fully on earth. This does not mean simply preaching about Christ. It means preaching the gospel of the kingdom; and the kingdom includes not only individuals and society but also the environment in which we live.

Matthew 4:12–22

Now when Jesus heard that John had been arrested, he withdrew into Galilee; and leaving Nazareth he went and dwelt in Capernaum by the sea, in the territory of Zebulun and Naphtali, that what was spoken by the prophet Isaiah might be fulfilled: 'The land of Zebulun and the land of Naphtali, toward the sea, across the Jordan, Galilee of the Gentiles—the people who sat in darkness have seen a great light, and for those who sat in the region of the shadow of death light has dawned.'

From that time Jesus began to preach, saying, 'Repent, for the kingdom of heaven is at hand.'

As he walked by the Sea of Galilee, he saw two brothers, Simon who is called Peter and Andrew his brother, casting a net into the sea; for they were fishermen. And he said to them 'Follow me, and I will make you fishers of men.' Immediately they left their nets and followed him. And going on from there he saw two other brothers, James the son of Zebedee and John his brother, in the boat with Zebedee their father, mending their nets, and he called them. Immediately they left the boat and their father, and followed him.

Comment on the reading

The arrest of John the Baptist, according to St Matthew, was the signal for the beginning of Jesus' public ministry, for until now Jesus had not preached publicly. Earlier, it seems that after his baptism at the hands of the Baptist, Jesus joined himself to John's mission, and had spent some time himself baptizing in Judea. 'Jesus and his disciples went into the land of Judea: there he remained with them and baptized. John also was baptizing at Aenon near Salim, because there was much water there' (John 3:22–23). At the arrest of John, we are told that he and his disciples went to the lake of Galilee, and 'they went into Capernaum' (Mark 1:21) which is on the lake, which he made, as it were, his local headquarters. This was the area where the tribes of Zebulun and Naphtali had lived before the exile. Matthew sees here a fulfilment of Isaiah 9:1f.: 'the land of Zebulun and the land of Naphtali, toward the sea, across the Jordan, Galilee of the Gentiles—the people who sat in darkness have seen a great light, and for those who sat in the region and shadow of death light has dawned' (Matthew 4:15–16). Galilee had not long been Jewish. There were still Gentiles living there, but the Galilean people had embraced the Jewish faith, and had done so with great enthusiasm, although not always with orthodoxy. Hence the appositeness of the quotation. The light alluded to in Isaiah is, of course, the light which Jesus and his good news brought.

John also had preached, 'Repent, for the kingdom of heaven is at hand' (Matthew 3:2). (Heaven was a way of referring to God, since the Jews regarded the name of God as too holy to use. So 'kingdom of heaven' means 'kingdom of God'.) John understood the arrival of the kingdom of heaven as the imminent coming of the day of judgment. According to Malachi 4:5, Elijah was to come before the 'great and terrible day of the Lord' to call people to repentance, and Jesus saw John's mission in that light. In one sense his mission was a continuation of John's, for he also preached, 'Repent, for the kingdom of heaven is at hand'. But for Jesus this did not mean the imminent end of the world. His message was not about the darkness of judgment, but about the good news of God's kingdom. His ministry was to inaugurate that kingdom which would be completed at the end of the age. Repentance was not emphasized: it was faith that mattered, and total commitment. 'Every one who has left houses or... father or mother or children or lands, for my name's sake, will receive a hundredfold, and inherit eternal life' (Matthew 19:29). Peter and Andrew followed him in faith immediately after their call to be his disciples, as also did James and John, who simply abandoned their nets to follow him.

Reflect and pray

Two thousand years ago Jesus called people to follow him. He calls them still. He gave his first disciples tasks to do. He gives us tasks to do today. He told them to proclaim God's kingly rule, and to share in it. He calls us to do the same. He called people to a change of heart. He calls us too.

Reflect that the risen Christ is always with us. His call to us is as real as it was to Peter and Andrew, and James and John. Then perhaps pray these prayers, or a different prayer of your own.

Jesus, I want to follow you all the days of my life. Show me what you want, and I will do it, with your help.

O God, please show me what I can do to help to restore the environment of your world. Help me to a change of heart, help me to understand, to see clearly and to think clearly. Amen.

2

Abusing God's creation

A horrible new strain of the rare Creutszfeldt-Jakob disease (CJD) in humans has appeared in the last twelve years. It seems to attack younger people, and it takes less time to develop. The sufferer gradually loses his memory, sinks into a coma, and dies. There is no cure.

No one has actually proved as yet a link with mad cow disease (BSE) but it seems probable from experiments with other animals. Most people think that the epidemic of BSE, now ten years old, was caused by a special type of cattle feed, which has also been used as fertilizer on cattle pastures. This was particularly rich in protein because it included the ground-up remains of both cattle and sheep.

Some sheep have long been infected by a similar illness called scrapie (non-infectious to humans). Experts believe that the infection has now jumped from one species to another. Scrapie, they think, has become BSE in cattle through the cattle feed and grass they have eaten, and BSE has become CJD in humans through their eating infected beef. These illnesses take a long time to develop, so no one can tell whether we shall suffer a huge epidemic of CJD or there will be only a few more cases. To prevent future infection, thousands of cattle have to be burnt. Until this is done, no one overseas wants to buy our beef. The beef industry is in ruins.

Cattle naturally eat only grass. If we are right about the origin of CJD, it has been caused by making them consume feed which contains remains of cattle and sheep. Herbivores have unwittingly been turned into carnivores, even cannibals. This shows a gross lack of respect for animals which we human beings have domesticated. It offends against the natural law of their being. It is a horrible offence for which, it seems, we may be horribly punished.

We have to ask ourselves whether we are treating the natural world today in such a way that we are in danger of bringing upon ourselves not blessings but a curse. God does not strike us directly; but he has so designed the natural world that if we do not respect its proper boundaries, the results rebound upon us. This is one of the spiritual truths to be found in the famous story of Adam and Eve. They were in charge of the Garden of Eden, but they disobeyed the rules of their stewardship. As a result they found that this disobedience rebounded on them: 'cursed is the ground because of you; in toil you shall eat of it all the days of your life' (Genesis 3:17).

It would be wrong to imagine that the curses mentioned in Deuteronomy were all literally fulfilled. But the Old Testament prophets insist that the Jews lost their inheritance in the Holy Land because they had not kept the commandments of God. These commandments were not for the most part concerned with the environment, or with cattle in particular. After all, they were spoken to the children of Israel in a very different situation thousands of years ago.

In those days no one could imagine that they were harming the environment. Much time was taken up in trying to ensure that the environment did not harm them. But the principle holds: if we disobey the natural laws of God, we must expect the judgment of God to come upon us. And this is what is happening today. We are abusing it, and suffering judgment as a result. Some of the correspondences are striking. 'Cursed shall be... the increase of your cattle, and the young of your flock.' That is precisely what many people today must be thinking about mad cow disease.

'Cursed shall you be in the city' we read. We are prepared to tolerate terrible conditions in our inner cities, and in the *favelas* and shanty towns of huge conurbations in other countries. The result? Huge increases in crime. For many it has indeed become a curse to live in such places.

'Cursed shall be the fruit of your body.' Well, not yet; but the mysterious drop in sperm count will affect birth rates if not stemmed. No one is certain what causes it. Some think it is due to the use of chemicals with particles which mimic elements in the human reproductive system. These chemicals are abroad in the environment, and may threaten not merely human reproduction, but that of animals as well.

As for the threat of diseases, this is all but upon us now, with a new deadly strain of staphylococcus which hospitals find so hard to eradicate and which only one antibiotic can touch. It seems the prodigal and unnecessary use of antibiotics has produced this new type of bacterium. In a rather similar way, patients who did not finish their course of TB treatment have brought about a new airborne strain of this disease which, it is said, is likely to kill 30 million people in the new decade. Again, advances due to the 'Green Revolution' have resulted in a great increase in cereal production. But these crops are deficient in trace minerals necessary to sustain human health.

The Israelites were threatened with 'fiery heat, and with drought'. Today we know about global warming, and the resulting climate change is already bringing in some places serious drought. 'The heavens over your head shall be brass'. The increasing number of skin cancers is caused by the shrinking ozone layer. Skin cancer is now second only to lung cancer in the UK. 'The earth under you shall be iron'. There is scientific evidence that artificial fertilizers are removing the natural fertility of the soil, overgrazing is producing desertification, and the cutting down of the world's forests results in the loss of topsoil and diminished fertility.

The children of Israel were told that, if they did not keep their covenant with God: 'The Lord will make the rain of your land powder and dust; from heaven it shall rain down upon you until you are destroyed.' We may not find powder and dust in our rainfall, but we do find some noxious chemicals. We have all heard of acid rain, caused by motor cars and by factory emissions. This harms our trees and kills fish in our rivers, because we prefer not to pay the cost of removing these pollutants at source.

In the Bible readings and comments that follow we shall be exploring these and other matters in greater detail. We shall be contrasting our present practices with biblical principles.

In the past the Church has been reluctant to concern itself with the environment. Our Christian leaders have not been warning us, and lay Christians have not been in the forefront of the battle.

We have been preaching the good news of God the Redeemer, and the saving message of Christ. We have rejoiced in God the Sanctifier, and the charismatic gifts of the Spirit. But we have tended to leave on one side God the Creator. We may have admired the beauty of nature, but we have ignored the laws of nature. We dare not forget that we worship not just God our Redeemer, but God who is also Creator and Sanctifier.

We speak of God in terms of Trinity, 'three persons and one God'. The triune God, the Father, Son and Holy Spirit, is our Creator, Redeemer and Sanctifier. God the Creator brought into being this unfathomable universe from the Big Bang onwards. There may be life elsewhere in the universe, but so far as we know here, alone among countless billions of stars, our planet has brought forth life. It has evolved with a wonderful stability built into it, so that we have taken for granted the purity of the air we breathe and the fertility of the earth and the oceans on which we rely for sustaining life.

In the recent past our knowledge of the natural world has increased beyond measure. Our technology has advanced enormously. We have learnt how to manipulate the natural world for our short-term use and convenience. We have used artificial fertilizers, pesticides and other chemical substances. We can even produce 'transgenic' plants and animals by transferring genes from one species to another. There has been relief from suffering and illness through medical advances, and greater abundance of foodstuffs and material comforts for a growing world population. But there are perils ahead.

We have to ask ourselves what will be the result of breaching the laws of nature. We have to consider whether, by crossing many thresholds of sustainability in the natural world for our short-term gain, we may be upsetting those delicate balances that have kept nature comfortable for life. This is a moral question, and our Christian faith is bound up with morality. This is one of the distinguishing features of Judeo-Christian religion.

The results will rebound on ourselves. When God made a covenant with the earth in the days of Noah (Genesis 9:12), he promised never again to exterminate mankind by a flood. But he did not promise that mankind would not exterminate itself by its abuse of the earth. It is possible that what God intended for us as a blessing we may, by our greed and folly, turn instead into a curse.

Deuteronomy 28:1–6, 13–24

'If you obey the voice of the Lord your God, being careful to do all his commandments which I command you this day, the Lord your God will set you high above all the nations of the earth. And all these blessings shall come upon you and overtake you, if you obey the voice of the Lord your God. Blessed shall you be in the city, and blessed shall you be in the field. Blessed shall be the fruit of your body, and the fruit of your ground, and the fruit of your beasts, the increase of your cattle, and the young of your flock. Blessed shall be your basket and your kneading-trough. Blessed shall you be when you come in, and blessed shall you be when you go out...

'And the Lord will make you the head, and not the tail; and you shall tend upward only, and not downward; if you obey the commandments of the Lord your God, which I command you this day, being careful to do them, and if you do not turn aside from any of the words which I command you this day, to the right hand or to the left, to go after other gods to serve them.

'But if you will not obey the voice of the Lord your God or be careful to do all his commandments and his statutes which I command you this day, then all these curses shall come upon you and overtake you. Cursed shall you be in the city, and cursed shall you be in the field. Cursed shall be your basket and your kneading-trough. Cursed shall be the fruit of your body, and the fruit of your ground, the increase of your cattle, and the young of your flock. Cursed shall you be when you come in, and cursed shall you be when you go out.

'The Lord will send upon you curses, confusion and frustration, in all that you undertake to do, until you are destroyed and perish quickly, on account of the evil of your doings, because you have forsaken me. The Lord will make the pestilence cleave to you until he has consumed you off the land which you are entering to take possession of it. The Lord will smite you with consumption, and with fever, inflammation, and fiery heat, and with drought, and with blasting, and with mildew; they shall pursue you until you perish. And the heavens over your head shall be brass, and the earth under you shall be iron. The Lord will make the rain of your land powder and dust; from heaven it shall come down upon you until you are destroyed.'

Comment on the reading

This passage is part of the ancient ritual which was to be carried out when the chosen people first entered the Promised Land. It was to take place as the children of Israel crossed the river Jordan, which marked its boundary. God had made a 'covenant' with them. They were to be reminded to keep their side of this agreement, with tremendous consequences if they did, and terrible consequences if they did not.

Instructions about what to do when they passed over the river Jordan were given by Moses. It must have been a deeply solemn occasion. In the previous chapter (27) we are told how, when they passed over the Jordan, they were to set up large stones. They were to plaster them, and write on them all the words of the Law, and then carry the stones up nearby Mount Ebal.

Any covenant, when it was ratified in the ancient word, ended with blessings if it was fulfilled and curses if it was infringed (see the end of the 'Book of the Covenant' in Exodus 23:20–33, or the end of the 'Holiness Code' in Leviticus 26:3–45). This took place in a particularly striking way on entry into the Promised Land. Opposite Mount Ebal stands Mount Gerizim. Six of the twelve tribes of Israel were to stand on Mount Gerizim to bless the people; and the other six tribes were to go up Mount Ebal opposite to curse the people. The Levites were to pronounce in a loud voice, so that everyone could hear, the words of the blessings if they kept the covenant and the curses that would follow if they didn't. It would have been a most impressive ritual.

These blessings and curses referred to the keeping of the Jewish Law, which is no longer (apart from the moral law) binding upon Christian people. Although they are no longer to be taken literally in any way, they remain a symbol for us today of something crucial to our well-being; the great blessings which follow if we keep to the natural law which God has implanted in our hearts, and the dreadful fate which can overcome us if we disobey it. The passage chosen for the reading centres on judgment. This follows inevitably on wrongdoing. The dire consequences of neglecting God's laws result in dreadful penalties.

A prayer

O Lord, I ask for your blessings on my life and on my dear ones. I ask for your blessings on my country and my nation. I know I am the child of God, for you have reconciled me to yourself through Christ. But I cannot receive your blessing if I knowingly transgress your laws. Nor can my country and nation receive your blessing if it knowingly transgresses the laws of your universe. Deliver us all from evil and save us from the curse that unthinking greed and selfishness brings upon us and upon our world.

3

Extinction of species

Some 530 million years ago in the so-called 'Cambrian Explosion', large numbers of different multicellular life forms first evolved. It is reckoned that since then some 30 billion different species have emerged. According to some estimates, there are some 30 million species existing today (only 1,390,902 are known to us). That means that 99.9 per cent of all species are now extinct. Species last from a million to 10 million years: the average lifespan is 4 million years. It is part of God's providence that, when circumstances change on earth, new forms of life become adapted to the new situation, and others die off, so species become extinct. Human beings have over 3 million years to go, on this analysis! Eventually, of course, all species will die because of the heat death of the planet, although that is millions and millions of years ahead.

On at least twenty occasions, according to the fossil record, there have been extinctions of species in which 15 to 40 per cent of all marine organisms perished. The causes are unknown, but were probably due to climate change. On five occasions there have been catastrophic extinctions. To qualify for inclusion in the Big Five, 65 per cent of all species must have become extinct. On one of these, at the end of the so called Permian Age about 250 million years ago, some 95 per cent of species disappeared! The last of the Big Five extinctions, which took place some 65 million years ago, was caused by the impact of a giant asteroid or comet. The dinosaurs perished then, fortunately for mankind, because a small rat-like mammal survived, from which we human beings have eventually evolved. (This shows how God takes risks. For some this remote but fortunate chance increases the probability that God so designed the universe that intelligent life would have evolved elsewhere in the universe as well.)

We are now on the verge of a sixth catastrophic extinction, which is different from all the others. This will have been caused exclusively by mankind, as the human race proliferates and changes the face of the planet.

It is difficult to know exactly how many species are being extinguished each year, because many of them are unknown to us as yet, and many never will be known, because they will have been exterminated. Responsible estimates of species extinctions have ranged up to 100,000 a year, and experts have predicted that within a century, if the present rates of extinction continue, half the species on the face of the earth will have disappeared. Everyone has heard of the threat to the giant panda, or certain species of whales, and other big animals. But few people realize that small plants and organisms are being destroyed by mankind at an unprecedented rate. We have only to look around us in the countryside to realize how we are becoming impoverished. Where are the cowslips and the buttercups? Where are the skylarks?

Why is this happening? The human race is expanding by 90 million people each year. In 1970 there were less than 2.5 billion people; but today there are some 5.7 billion people alive on the earth, and the figure is set to increase still further. We shall be looking at this in greater detail in the next chapter.

That number of people takes a lot of feeding! All available land has to be set aside for food production in most countries. Add to this the human instinct for collecting rare species, and our exploitation of wild animals and fish for food. Again, you have to add the effect of the introduction of alien species which can so often lead to the extermination of native animals: in most parts of England, for example, we no longer see the red squirrel.

When a population of wildlife is reduced to small numbers, its eventual extinction is guaranteed. It is vulnerable to fluctuations in its numbers, which may be caused by disease or disaster. A large population can withstand a sudden drop in its numbers: a small population cannot. Once a low threshold of numbers is passed, a species is doomed.

Half the world's species live in the tropical rainforests. These are disappearing at an unprecedented rate. Most of them are still unknown, but we can estimate their number from those areas of forest we do know. (We shall also be looking at this subject later.) The rain forests are being cut down at the rate of 2 per cent a year (we can now be certain of these figures through satellite observation). When the habitat of the plants and animals in the rainforests disappear, so do the plants and animals too.

All species (probably including our own) are bound to die off sooner or later. Does it really matter if we assist that process?

Animals are our kith and kin. We evolved from the world of nature, and we have a natural kinship with it. According to the story in Genesis of the creation of Adam, 'God said, "It is not good that the man should be alone; I will make him a helper fit for him." So God formed every beast of the field and every bird of the air, and brought them to the man to see what he would call them' (Genesis 2:18–19). It was only when these were found to be inadequate for this purpose, that (according to the story) Eve was made out of Adam's rib. The passage shows the natural kinship between mankind and the natural world. Animals and birds cannot act as companions to human beings in the way that other humans can; but they have a definite relationship with us humans, as can be seen in the way many keep them as pets.

Animals and plants are part of God's world which he has brought into being. They are part of the variety and the beauty of the world we have inherited. We read in the scriptures that God takes delight in them. 'There go the ships, and Leviathan which thou didst form to sport in it' (Psalm 104:26). The obedience of animals to the divine will is contrasted with the disobedience of men: 'Even the stork in the heavens knows her times; and the turtle dove, swallow, and crane keep the time of their coming; but my people know not the ordinance of the Lord' (Jeremiah 8:7). The animal world has value for God, otherwise he would not have allowed it to evolve.

Human beings are different. God has given mankind dominion over nature because we are made in God's image. 'Then God said, "Let us make man in our image, after our likeness; and let them have dominion over the fish of the sea, and over the birds of the air, and over the cattle, and over all the earth, and over every creeping thing that creeps upon the earth"' (Genesis 1:26). So we may use the kingdoms of plants and animals for our benefit, and kill them for our use, so long as we do not abuse this privilege by causing unnecessary pain and suffering. But this domination does not extend to whole species. It may be within the plan of the Creator that there should be extinctions of species; but it is not right that human beings should play God and exterminate them. Once a species is gone, it is irrecoverable.

All living things are interdependent. Our ability to sustain human life depends on many other species. The natural sciences are teaching us to look at life more holistically, that is to say, viewing it as a whole rather than looking at each part separately. The science of ecology is showing us the need for biodiversity, with various differences between species. Life on earth acts as an interactive whole. It is this that produces a stable and healthy living world. We know we need other species, but we don't as yet know exactly which species are vital. If human beings act like a privileged élite which kills off species at will, this will rebound upon us.

We need biodiversity on earth. Climate and other conditions

may change, and new types of plants may be needed which can only be found in the wild; but if species have been extinguished, they may no longer exist. There is huge potential value in the vast numbers of species which are being extinguished. They could be the source of new or improved crops. They could provide us with new materials. They could help to heal human sickness and illness by providing us with new medicines. All this has happened in the past, and would continue in the future if biodiversity were preserved.

Our thoughtless search for short-term gain is denying our children and all posterity the richness and wealth of the natural world which we have inherited.

Genesis 6:11–22

> Now the earth was corrupt in God's sight, and the earth was filled with violence. And God saw the earth, and behold, it was corrupt; for all flesh had corrupted their way upon the earth. And God said to Noah, 'I have determined to make an end of all flesh; for the earth is filled with violence through them; behold, I will destroy them with the earth. Make yourself an ark of gopher wood... and cover it inside and out with pitch. This is how you are to make it: the length of the ark three hundred cubits, its breadth fifty cubits, and its height thirty cubits. Make a roof for the ark, and finish it to a cubit above; and set the door of the ark in its side; make it with lower, second, and third decks. For behold, I will bring a flood of waters upon the earth, to destroy all flesh in which is the breath of life from under heaven; everything that is on the earth shall die. But I will establish my covenant with you; and you shall come into the ark, you, your sons, your wife, and your sons' wives with you. And of every living thing of all flesh, you shall bring two of every sort into the ark, to keep them alive with you; they shall be male and female. Of the birds according to

their kinds, and of the animals according to their kinds, of every creeping thing of the ground according to its kind, two of every sort shall come in to you, to keep them alive. Also take with you every sort of food that is eaten, and store it up; and it shall serve as food for you and for them.' Noah did this; he did all that God commanded him.

Comment on the reading

The story of the flood has fascinated Bible readers, in particular children. It is a story both of punishment (of those who died in the flood) and of mercy (because God did not make a full end).

Literary critics have explained that the story in Genesis is a conflation of two separate accounts of the flood. This accounts for some repetitions, and it is possible to make two separate accounts out of the one narrative. But this makes little difference to the spiritual meaning of the story.

Some who have taken the account literally have searched for the lost ark on Mount Ararat. This, however, is to miss the point of the story. Literalists have also believed that there was a universal flood over the whole planet. Sea shells and fossils of fish high up on mountains were thought to support this, until it was realized that these were caused by massive upheavals on the surface of the planet. Ancient Babylonian tablets and Sumerian records also recount a flood, and clearly the story refers to a local inundation in that region. The Tigris-Euphrates valley was subject to severe river floods.

The spiritual meaning of the story is twofold. In the first place it is God's judgment on the evil of his world. It is interesting to note that this involved not just mankind but all creation. The other meaning of the story is the more important for our purposes here. God intended mass extinctions in the flood but he did not intend to make a full end. The flood was not to frustrate his purpose in creating the world. The inclusion of male and female of each species in the ark clearly implies that each species was intended to breed after the flood had subsided and the living creatures were released.

It was not only animals useful to mankind that were preserved. All birds, insects and beasts were included because God had created them all, and 'God saw that it was good' (Genesis 1:25). The raven and the dove which were released from the ark to find out if the waters had subsided were not domesticated birds. All living things have intrinsic value in the eyes of God. There are in the scriptures many appreciative remarks about wild animals (Psalm 104:10–22; Jeremiah 8:7; Matthew 10:29). There is even an instruction for those taking eggs or fledglings from a bird's nest to spare the mother bird, so that she may continue to breed (Deuteronomy 22:6f.).

A prayer

Lord, may we love all your creation, all the earth and every grain of sand in it. May we love every leaf, every ray of your light. May we love the animals: you have given them the rudiments of thought and joy untroubled. Let us not trouble them; let us not harass them, let us not deprive them of their happiness, let us not work against your intent. For we acknowledge to you that all is like an ocean, all is flowing and blending, and that to withhold any measure of love from anything in your universe is to withhold that same measure from you.

Adapted from Fyodor Dostoyevsky, *The Brothers Karamazov*

4

The trees of the forest

In the ancient world a tree was a symbol of strength. Today man-made products such as steel and concrete have taken on that role. In most of the world, trees, for all their natural beauty, are now thought of in economic terms—for their financial value when they have been cut down.

In fact they play a vital part in keeping our planet comfortable for life. Tropical rain forests comprise 6 per cent of the world's land surface. They enable rain clouds to form. They cool the climate. They keep the topsoil from blowing away or being lost through run-off after rain. They provide a habitat for plants and animals not found elsewhere. It is worth looking at these in greater detail.

When we breathe, we breathe in oxygen, and breathe out moisture and carbon dioxide. Trees do the opposite. They suck up huge amounts of moisture from the earth through their deep roots. They return it to the atmosphere through what is called evapotranspiration, that is, through their leaves. This enables the recycling of water from the sky to the land and back again to the sky. Clouds then return the moisture from the atmosphere to the land. Without evapotranspiration it would be difficult for rain clouds to form, and as a result even ocean currents could alter. Where forests have been cut down, the climate changes. Rain is scarce. The sun beats down unrelentingly from a clear sky; and the result is dereliction.

Carbon dioxide in the atmosphere needs recycling too. Trees provide an important way in which this happens. They break it up into carbon and oxygen. The carbon is turned into the wood of the tree. The oxygen is returned to the atmosphere through the green leaves by a process known as photosynthesis. This helps to keep the balance of nature comfortable for us.

The tropical rainforests provide a way of life and a culture for the indigenous people who live in them. When the forests have been cut down, they have nowhere to go, and their culture is destroyed. They become a prey to the illnesses of civilized societies, to which they have no natural immunity; and so most of them die. Some of them have actually been murdered by those intent on cutting down some of the rainforests of South America where they live.

The tall trees of the rainforest provide a canopy which prevents the rain from tropical storms ruining the fertility of the earth by a violent run-off which takes away the precious topsoil. The roots of the trees bind the soil. Otherwise the friable earth becomes eroded. The earth beneath the trees is not naturally fertile. After tropical forests have been cut down, it tends to provide very poor grazing land.

The tree canopy not only breaks up the downpour when it rains: it also keeps out the sun, and provides shade and coolness in a tropical climate. As a result, to use the words of scripture, 'the birds of the air and the beasts of the field shelter under its branches' (Ezekiel 31:6; cf. Matthew 13:32). The tree canopy also enables many otherwise unknown plants to flourish. Half the total species of living things come from the tropical rainforests.

Twenty new species of birds have been found in the tropical rainforests of South America in the last ten years. There must be many more elsewhere which are still unknown. Whole species may have been extinguished before they could be known. There are many, many species of insects and other animals. The International Union for the Conservation of

Nature and Natural Resources keeps track of species that are known. It publishes a Red Book of endangered and extinguished species.

Many much-loved and nutritious foods originated from the rainforests. This is where tomatoes originally came from, and pineapples and cocoa and rice.

The tropical rain forest has been a wonderful source of new medicines. This is the origin of quinine (for malaria), curare (muscle relaxant for operations) and vincristine (for leukaemia). Seventy per cent of plants with anti-cancer properties come from the rainforest. Chemicals used for the treatment of bronchitis, laryngitis and epilepsy come from the same source. There are many more drugs to be discovered. It will be tragic if they are lost to us for ever.

The rainforests are disappearing at an alarming rate. There were some 15.3 billion acres of undisturbed primary forest before agriculture began. The best estimate is that only 3.7 billion acres remain. Some 37 million acres are lost each year. It is claimed that some of this will be replaced. Schemes have been set up for logging projects and reforestation; but voluntary societies have shown that the forests continue to be felled. In any case replanted areas cannot begin to compete with the richness and diversity of the primary forest. What is needed is sustainable development, with replanting taking place within existing forests.

Unless we stop now, by the year 2006, 65 per cent of all the forests of the tropics will have gone. When 70 per cent of an ecosystem is destroyed, the rest cannot sustain the environment necessary for its survival. An emergency situation is therefore developing. Dr James Lovelock, FRS, an eminent scientist, has likened it to exfoliation, the destruction of the earth's living skin. To lose 75 per cent of human skin is fatal. Like skin, the forests 'sweat' to keep us cool. The humid warm atmosphere provides just the right environment for the trees to grow. Without the 'sweat' from the trees, there will be no rain, and these areas become scrub or desert.

Much of Europe was once covered with forest. We cut it down, and it provided timber for naval vessels and much else. Developing nations are often burdened with debt and badly need cash. Naturally their peoples want to increase their standard of living. 'We want to cut down our forests,' they say. 'Look at what you have done in the West. You are in no position to say that we shouldn't.' So they create ranches to produce more food for the world's growing population, they erect paper mills and they sell the timber.

But the tragedy is that these countries are living on their capital. It has been shown that 2.5 acres of a tropical forest in Peru could produce in non-timber products far more than the cash value of its felled timber. And once the timber has gone, the species are lost, and the area becomes a waste land. When the forests have gone, the climate will have changed and crops cannot be grown. Developing countries need to be persuaded that it is in their own interests not to live on their capital by cutting down their rainforests.

But we live in the developed world. What can we do about it? It would help if the North would remit some of the Third World's debt, perhaps under a 'Debt for Conservation' scheme. We need to reduce our demand for hardwoods. If we recycled our paper, this would save importing pulp for paper. If we photocopied on both sides of the page, more still would be saved. We could use more plastic substitutes for wood. We could cut out waste. We could enquire before we buy furniture where the wood comes from: if it comes from tropical rainforests, we could refuse to buy it. We could refuse ever to buy mahogany, even for lavatory seats.

Most of the timber felled in the tropical rain forests is sold to developed countries. If there was no market for this, there would be little point in destroying the forests. It is easy to blame the developing countries. We forget that the developed countries usually provide the market for their goods. Although population is burgeoning in developing countries, the developed world consumes two-thirds of the world's resources.

According to a parable of the prophet Ezekiel, God cut down a beautiful giant cedar tree because it represented Pharaoh and the people of Egypt, a proud nation which would not recognize God. With us, it is the other way round. We human beings are cutting down our forest trees. We do it because we are proud too, taking pride in our own self-sufficiency, and we do not realize that they are vitally important for the well-being of our planet. Here is an important point we have in common with those ancient Egyptians against whom Ezekiel was prophesying. We too are proud and we do not recognize the gift of our Creator God.

Ezekiel 31:1–14

In the eleventh year, in the third month, on the first day of the month, the word of the Lord came to me: 'Son of man, say to Pharaoh king of Egypt and to his multitude:

'Whom are you like in your greatness? Behold, I will liken you to a cedar in Lebanon, with fair branches and forest shade, and of great height, its top among the clouds. The waters nourished it, the deep made it grow tall, making its rivers flow round the place of its planting, sending forth its streams to all the trees of the forest. So it towered high among all the trees of the forest; its boughs grew large and its branches long, from abundant water in its shoots. All the birds of the air made their nests in its boughs; under its branches all the beasts of the field brought forth their young; and under its shadow dwelt all the great nations. It was beautiful in its greatness, in the length of its branches; for its roots went down to abundant waters. The cedars in the garden of God could not rival it, nor the fir trees equal its boughs; the plane trees were as nothing compared with its branches; no tree in the garden of God was like it in beauty. I made it beautiful in the mass of its branches, and all the trees of Eden envied it, that were in the garden of God.

'Therefore thus says the Lord God: Because it towered high and set its top among the clouds, and its heart was proud of its height, I will give it into the hands of a mighty one of the nations; he shall surely deal with it as its wickedness deserves... Foreigners, the most terrible of the nations, will cut it down and leave it. On the mountains and in all the valleys its branches will fall, and its boughs will lie broken in all the watercourses of the land; and all the peoples of the earth will go from its shadow and leave it. Upon its ruin will dwell all the birds of the air, and upon its branches will be all the beasts of the field. All this is in order that no trees by the waters may grow to lofty height or set their tops among the clouds, and that no trees that drink water may reach up to them in height; for they are all given over to death, to the nether world among mortal men, with those who go down to the Pit.

Comment on the reading

This prophecy of Ezekiel forms the fifth of seven prophecies against Egypt. It is precisely dated to May 587BC. It is very dramatic and vivid. Egypt as a great world power is compared to a huge cedar, and its downfall is prophesied due to its pride and its failure to accept that God has made it what it is.

Ezekiel had earlier used the imagery of a tree to make clear his message. He had earlier prophesied: 'I myself will take a sprig from the lofty top of the cedar, and will set it out... and I myself will plant it upon a high and lofty mountain... that it may bring forth boughs and bear fruit, and become a noble cedar; and under it will dwell all kinds of beasts; in the shade of its branches birds of every kind will nest. And all the trees of the field shall know that I the Lord bring low the high tree, and make high the low tree' (Ezekiel 17:22–24). The same imagery is taken up in the New Testament in the words of Jesus himself in his parable of the mustard seed (Mark 4:30–32 and parallels).

The imagery of a cedar tree and its fall is also found in Isaiah, where it refers to the fall not of Egypt but of Babylon: 'The whole earth is at rest and quiet; they break forth into singing. The cypresses rejoice at you, the cedars of Lebanon, saying, "Since you were laid low, no hewer comes up against us"' (Isaiah 14:7–8). Possibly this originally referred to the fall of Assyria.

A similar theme is found in king Nebuchadnezzar's dream which Daniel interprets as referring to the king: 'The visions of my head as I lay in bed were these: I saw, and behold, a tree in the midst of the earth; and its height was great. The tree grew and became strong, and its top reached to heaven, and it was visible to the end of the whole earth. Its leaves were fair and its fruit abundant... The beasts of the field found shade under it, and the birds of the air dwelt in its branches, and all flesh was fed from it. I saw in the visions of my head as I lay in bed, and behold, a watcher, a holy one, came down from heaven. He cried aloud and said thus, "Hew down the tree and cut off its branches, strip off its leaves and scatter its fruit; let the beasts flee from under it and the birds from its branches"' (Daniel 4:10–14). This imagery is thought to be derived from an ancient myth of a world tree, which reached from the depths below to the heights of heaven.

The imagery of a tree goes back a long way. Ezekiel's prophecy against Egypt certainly contains references to ancient motifs and symbols. He speaks of 'Eden, the garden of God' (Ezekiel 31:9), where we are told in Genesis that 'God made to grow every tree that is pleasant to the sight and good for food' (Genesis 2:9).

Although the passage is an allegory, it has been selected here because it gives a vivid impression of the huge trees in the forests of the ancient world, their habitat for wildlife, and the catastrophic result of their felling. The importance of water for the welfare of trees is also stressed by Ezekiel (cf. Psalm 1:3: 'He is like a tree planted by streams of water, that yields its fruit in its season, and its leaf does not wither'). Trees were, of course, cut down in the ancient world, as for example, by Hiram king of Tyre for the building of the first temple in Jerusalem: 'So Hiram supplied Solomon with all the timber of cedar and cypress that he desired' (1 Kings 5:10). Assyria too felled timber for weapons of war: 'With my many chariots I have gone up the heights of the mountains, to the far recesses of Lebanon; I felled its tallest cedars' (Isaiah 37:24); but, unlike today, the felling was on a comparatively small scale, so that the forests would naturally regenerate.

Reflect and pray

My aspens dear, whose airy cages quelled,
Quelled or quenched in leaves the leaping sun,
All felled, felled, are all felled;
Of a fresh and following folded rank
Not spared, not one
That dandled a sandalled
Shadow that swam or sank
On meadow and river and wind-wandering weed-winding bank.

O if we but knew what we do
When we delve or hew—
Hack and rack the growing green!
Since country is so tender
To touch, her being so slender,
That, like this sleek and seeing ball
But a prick will make no eye at all,
Where we, even where we mean
To mend her we end her,

When we hew or delve:
Aftercomers cannot guess the beauty been.
Ten or twelve, only ten or twelve
Strokes of havoc unselve
The sweet especial scene,
Rural scene, a rural scene,
Sweet especial rural scene.

Gerard Manley Hopkins, 'Binsey Poplars felled 1879'

Blessed art thou, O Lord King of the universe, for the trees and the fruit of the trees.

from 'Blessings' in the *Jewish Sephardi Daily Prayerbook*

5

The water of life

We call our planet 'earth', but seven-tenths of its surface is water. Compared with the diameter of the planet, this is only like a thin film over its surface. But the oceans greatly influence life on earth. They are salty, and a self-assembling mechanism ensures that they are kept at their present level of 3.4 per cent salt (by weight); and so the fish and other marine organisms that are specially adapted to this habitat can flourish in the oceans.

The oceans have a very large influence on weather and climate. They form an important link in the sulphur cycle, as large quantities of this element are washed into the sea in rivers. It needs to be returned to land. In the oceans marine algae and other organisms emit large quantities of dimethyl sulphate gas, which has that distinctive smell associated with the sea. Rapid oxidation of this gas over the oceans produces sulphuric acid droplets which enable the water vapour to condense to form clouds. Without this, they cannot. When the clouds drop rain over land, the sulphur is returned to earth. This is typical of the recycling which provides stability to life on earth. The clouds in turn affect weather and climate.

The oceans also have an effect on land climate through currents of water which bring cold water into warmer areas, and vice versa. Without the Gulf Stream, the climate of the United Kingdom would be arctic. Beneath the surface vast masses of placid water stabilize the climate. It is important that mankind does not interfere with these natural processes.

The oceans can absorb vast quantities of various gases. For example, they have the vital role of absorbing carbon dioxide, and so they help to keep the planet comfortably cool.

The oceans are becoming polluted. Estuaries and continental shelves provide good breeding grounds for fish. But pollution is worse near the shore. This is where nutrients from land fertilizers, swept down rivers, emerge into the sea. They can make small marine organisms bloom. These use up the oxygen in the water and the fish suffocate. Sometimes they are poisonous, and we have to be warned not to eat shellfish. Untreated sewage from coastal towns may be discharged into the sea. This makes bathing not only filthy but dangerous. Chemical works may dump large quantities of toxic materials into the ocean.

Oil slicks kill birds and marine organisms. Some synthetic compounds do not break down in sea water. Synthetic chemicals known as DDT (a chlorinated hydrocarbon) and PCBs (polychlorinated biphenyls) upset the endocrine systems of organisms, causing premature births and spontaneous abortions in sea-lions in California, and have interfered with the reproductive systems of species such as gulls and bald eagles, as residues accumulate exponentially high up the food chain, as one species feeds on contaminated species lower in the food chain. Despite controls, there can still be high levels of toxic minerals around estuaries or inland lakes and seas.

Another cause of pollution is persistent litter on the high seas. In 1988, 1,000 tons of litter were removed from 2,000 miles of Californian coastline! Sixty-two per cent of this was plastic. Death of marine animals can be caused by entanglement or ingestion. 30,000 fur seals are reported to be dying annually in the North Pacific from entanglement with discarded fishing gear. Similarly 60,000 animals are killed off the coast of Norway. No one knows the effect of pollutants on the immune system. Some years ago 18,000 seals died in the Baltic and North Sea of a virus infection, and it was suspected that pollution had lessened their ability to resist the infection.

The worst pollution occurs near centres of industrial activity. The North Sea receives pollution from many European countries. Spectacular red blooms have resulted from the 'eutrophication' (overnourishment) of algae.

Another badly polluted area is the Mediterranean. This is an almost land-locked area with no tides. There are algal blooms, deterioration of fish stocks and evidence of industrial pollution.

It is dangerous to sink radioactive wastes in the seabed. However safe their containment may be in the short-term, they are likely to remain toxic for longer than their containers can be guaranteed to last. Although Britain has discontinued this, its past practices may produce future hazards.

Fish and other marine products provide 16 per cent of mankind's animal protein intake, and 5.6 per cent of total animal protein. In Asia, 1 billion people rely on fish for their primary source of animal protein. But fish stocks are falling. In all but two of the fifteen major marine fishing regions the catch has fallen since 1988, and in one of them by 30 per cent. Once considered the poor man's diet, fish is now in some areas becoming a luxury food.

The world fish catch, which increased fourfold over forty years, is now declining. Some time ago, it was estimated that oceanic fisheries could not sustain a yield of more than 100 million tons a year. It reached that point in 1989 and since then has declined. Pollution accounts for part of this; but it is mostly due to overfishing. Unless fishing is better regulated, it will continue to decline. Despite the world's increasing population, we have passed the threshold of sustainable yield. Marine fish farming often exacerbates the problem. Mangrove swamps are removed, and ground up fish meal from the oceans are given to the farmed fish!

What of fresh water? Two-thirds of all the water extracted from rivers and underground aquifers is used for irrigation. But the need for water by an ever increasing world population is reducing the amount available for agriculture. In many places (China in particular) water tables are falling. In Britain, much water is wasted, mainly through leaking pipes. The demand for fresh water generally is becoming unsustainable, as water is withdrawn from underground aquifers at a higher rate than can be replaced. If the planet warms up, there will be more changes in climate which may result in less rain.

In most industrial countries the fish catch from inland waters has collapsed, and continues at an unsustainable level, partly through overfishing and partly through the destruction of ecosystems on which the fish depend. As larger fish disappear, the total weight of catch may be sustained for a time by a larger number of smaller fish. If these are caught before reproducing themselves, the downward spiral will continue. Fish farms are likely to be more successful in fresh water milieux.

Much of the pollution which reaches the oceans comes down the rivers, which are also polluted. Rivers have always been used for drinking, as sewers, for food and for transport and also as waste dumps. Partly through the work of the (now superseded) National Rivers Authority, the health of rivers in the UK has greatly increased over the last thirty years. We now have the right to find out what is in our tap water: the privatized supplier has to provide this free of charge. Laws are quite strict against pollution, although breaches of them still take place.

There is growing public awareness of these problems. At the same time there is growing resistance. People object to restrictions imposed by the European Community on local marine fishing grounds. There is opposition to higher water rates needed to make domestic supplies more efficient. Few people respond to calls for economy in the use of water. Such is human nature that controls on water pollution, water use and overfishing generally have to be imposed by law. In general people should pay for the pollution they cause. However great the short-term need, we should not go beyond sustainable thresholds of fishing stocks, which may prevent their regeneration. British people are aware that cod and herring are now expensive, and out of reach of many, whereas they used to be cheap and plentiful.

Psalm 104:1–13, 16, 24–26

Bless the Lord, O my soul! O Lord my God, thou art very great! Thou art clothed with honour and majesty, who coverest thyself with light as with a garment, who hast stretched out the heavens like a tent, who has laid the beams of thy chambers on the waters, who makest the clouds thy chariot, who ridest on the wings of the wind, who makest the winds thy messengers, fire and flame thy ministers.

Thou didst set the earth on its foundations, so that it should never be shaken. Thou didst cover it with the deep as with a garment; the waters stood above the mountains. At thy rebuke they fled; at the sound of thy thunder they took to flight. The mountains rose, the valleys sank down to the place for which thou didst appoint for them. Thou didst set a bound which they should not pass, so that they might not again cover the earth.

Thou makest springs gush forth in the valleys; they flow between the hills, they give drink to every beast of the field; the wild asses quench their thirst. By them the birds of the air have their habitation; they sing among the branches. From thy lofty abode thou waterest the mountains; the earth is satisfied with the fruit of thy work...

The trees of the Lord are watered abundantly, the cedars of Lebanon which he planted. In them the birds build their nests; the stork has her home in the fir trees...

O Lord, how manifold are thy works! In wisdom hast thou made them all; the earth is full of thy creatures. Yonder is the sea, great and wide, which teems with things innumerable, living things both small and great. There go the ships, and Leviathan which thou didst form to sport in it.

Comment on the reading

Psalm 104 is a poetic account of creation in the form of a thanksgiving to God. It is based on the creation story of Genesis 1, and it follows the six days of creation. Its cosmology reflects the pre-scientific age in which it was written. It contains deep insights and spiritual truths. It is in some ways like the Egyptian 'Hymn to Aton' of the fourteenth century BC, but it is most probably independent. It shows the distinctive mark of the Jewish faith: all is dependent on the graciousness of God. This reading has been chosen to illustrate the theme of water, to which the psalm gives very great emphasis.

In the creation story, water is pre-existent to the creation. 'The earth was without form and void, and darkness was upon the face of the deep' (Genesis 1:2). God began by creating light, the first day's work of creation (vv. 1–4). Then he created the firmament of heaven, by dividing the pre-existent waters, with the upper waters above heaven, and the lower waters below the earth (vv. 5–9); the work of the second day. At first the lower waters covered the highest mountains—'thou didst cover it with the deep as with a garment'—but God had subdued them, and they sank so that the mountains appeared and the earth was firmly settled (vv. 5–9). The psalm makes it clear that all living things, beasts and birds and trees, are dependent upon water, without which they cannot live (vv. 10–13). So God made springs in the valleys and provides water for the life which he has created.

Rivers provide fresh water; but God has also provided the sea, where there is another creation, teeming with innumerable forms of life, both large and small, including the great sea monsters (vv. 25f.) (The great sea monsters are particularly included in the story of the creation in Genesis 1:21.) Leviathan has been identified with the sea monster Tiamat in the Babylonian creation story; but here again the story carries the characteristic Jewish mark of God's rule over all creation, and his setting of boundaries which should not be passed.

In a dry land it was natural that the theme of water should be stressed. It is a natural Christian symbol. It symbolizes the washing away of sin. 'You were washed, you were sanctified...' wrote St Paul to the Corinthians (1 Corinthians 6:11). 'He saved us... in virtue of his own mercy, by the washing of regeneration and renewal in the Holy Spirit', we read in Titus 3:5. We are baptized into the death of Christ that we may share in his resurrection according to St Paul: 'we were buried therefore with him by baptism into death, so that as Christ was raised from the dead by the glory of the Father, we too might walk in newness of life' (Romans 6:4). When Christians are baptized, it is as though we return to the waters of the womb in order to be reborn anew in Christ. Water is a natural symbol of regeneration. According to John, Jesus said to the Samaritan woman, 'The water that I shall give him will become in him a spring of water welling up to eternal life' (John 4:14). It is natural to use water as a symbol of eternal life since water is a necessity of all life.

To think about

Think about what happens to grass when there is no rain. Picture it in your mind's eye. If you have ever seen pictures of cattle, near to death or dying through lack of water, think about them. Think about a house plant that died because you forgot to water it. Think about one reviving because you remembered in time. Think about the water that runs from your tap when you turn it on. Think about women in the Two-Thirds World walking for miles to get water and then carrying it home on their heads. Think about fish floating on the surface of a river, dead because the water was polluted. Then reflect on this biblical image of the water of life:

'Then he showed me the river of the water of life, bright as crystal, flowing from the throne of God and of the Lamb through the middle of the street of the city; also, on either side of the river, the tree of life with its twelve kinds of fruit, yielding its fruit each month; and the leaves of the tree were for the healing of the nations.'

Revelation 22:1–2

6
World population

World population, during the last 200 years, has been increasing at a phenomenal rate. A couple of centuries ago it was half a billion. It is now 5.7 billion. It is increasing today, as we have seen, by 90 million a year. This is the equivalent of the entire population of the United Kingdom, Ireland, Benelux and Denmark!

World population increase has peaked, but still shows huge increases. For the future, the United Nations gives low, medium and high projections. For the year 2000, the figures are 6.1, 6.3 and 6.4 billion. The differences seem small, even though they would involve 300 million people. But follow through this projection to the year 2050, and you get the following projections: 7.9, 9.8 and 11.9 billion (over twice the present population). That is, of course, barring disaster, for there may be catastrophic famines before then.

The world population increase has several causes. There have been huge medical advances, so that far fewer babies die in infancy. The expectation of life has vastly increased, so that we have greater death control without greater birth control. There have, so far, been huge increases in agricultural production to support this growing world population, and the world economy has developed to provide jobs.

Thomas Robert Malthus (1766–1834), while still a curate in Surrey, published his 'Essay in Population' in which he pointed out that births increase in geometrical progression, but food only in arithmetic progression. It was thought that advances in agricultural technology would nullify this distinction. So far it has. But not for much longer. Despite official United Nations predictions of increases in food production, for the last three years world tonnage of crops has actually decreased. There are at the moment only forty-eight days of world reserves for cereal foods, which form the world's staple diet.

What effects does this great surge in human population have? We have already seen that it is resulting in a mass extinction of species, due to the need to feed millions more mouths each year. People need fire for warmth and cooking; and so brushwood and trees are becoming denuded, and topsoil as a result is eroded, with resultant climate changes. The strain on resources of many kinds is very great. Energy use is increasing. Water levels are falling throughout most of the world. Fish levels are falling. Pollution is increasing. Desertification is growing. Overpopulation is also causing mass migrations to the towns and cities, so that many Third World cities consist of makeshift homes, abject poverty, social disintegration and crime.

Some countries have tried to tempt people to have smaller families by tax disincentives, or by giving free education to small families. It seems unfair to deprive innocent children in this way. India for a time attempted physical controls, with compulsory sterilization; but this was unacceptable to the people.

China, which has huge overpopulation problems, restricts families to only one child each, with strict community supervision. This may be possible in an authoritarian communist state but it is unacceptable elsewhere. The desire to reproduce is a basic human instinct. The decision to have children is a very personal one between husband and wife. It must not, in Christian conscience, be imposed by the state. Population policies must be acceptable to the individuals concerned.

If we look at population projections region by region, Africa—the poorest region—is far and away at the top of the world league. Then comes Asia, next India, then China, then Latin America and finally the developed world. In the countries of the developed world, deaths and births are already in balance. In Britain, there are actually more deaths than births.

Why is there this great difference between regions? When people have a higher standard of living, they want fewer children. In undeveloped countries, where there are no national systems of benefit, children are an insurance for old age, as well as unpaid labour on smallholdings. Where the standard of living is low, more children die in infancy, and so parents tend to have larger families in case many of their children die. Again, in poor countries there are often no available facilities for contraception. Millions of women want it, but can't get it.

There is one further factor, and it is the most important. When women have the opportunity to be educated, they want more to life than bearing and bringing up their children. It is generally agreed that the key to population control lies with the empowerment of women.

All churches agree on the need to reduce or at least stabilize world population. But official Roman Catholic teaching holds that each and every act of human intercourse should be open to conception. Therefore, according to this teaching, any form of artificial contraception is wrong. This would seem to be a great hindrance to population control. However, statistics in the developed world show little difference between predominantly Roman Catholic and Protestant countries, suggesting that the ruling is not generally observed. It may be different in Two-Thirds-World countries where natural delight in fertility has been particularly strong.

Other churches (such as the Anglican Church) believe that children are the natural fruit of marriage, but that married life as a whole should be open to conception rather than each and every act of intercourse.

In 1994 there was in Cairo an important world conference

staged by the United Nations on Population and Development. Global goals for the year 2015 included universal access to family planning, information and services, and a 71 per cent contraceptive prevalence. It was also hoped to reduce the infant mortality rate from a maximum of sixty-two to twelve infants per 1,000 and to give access to primary education to all.

The planet obviously cannot support more people than it can feed. If world population is not stabilized, nature will see that this happens. Already many are hungry, or die of hunger or from diseases caused by undernourishment. This will happen to many more. Famine will become more widespread, and even catastrophic, until food and population are again in balance. Meanwhile irreparable damage will have been done to the environment.

There is no cause for us in Britain to feel complacent about world population because our supermarkets are bursting with goods and our deaths slightly outnumber our births. We give comparatively little in aid to developing countries, and the recent new GATT trade agreement is of little help to the undeveloped world.

Yet stabilization of world population is closely connected with Two-Thirds-World aid and trade. Transfers of technology would enable a higher standard of living. If people were able to live above subsistence level, more money would be available for the education of women. Some form of national benefits for the needy could even be introduced. Medical services would improve, so that fewer children would die in childbirth and in infancy. Contraception would be more readily available.

In some countries abortion is used as a means of birth restriction. The scriptures have no definite teaching on this subject, and although Christians are divided about therapeutic abortion, all are agreed that it is sinful to kill human life developing in the womb simply in order to restrict live births. Christians are divided also over the morality of artificial contraception, the official teaching of the Roman Catholic Church forbidding it. There is naturally nothing to be found in the scriptures for or against it, for when they were written there were no problems of overpopulation; but most Christians regard its use as falling into the category of a wise stewardship of human resources. Jesus taught that one of the two great commandments was: 'You shall love your neighbour as yourself' (Leviticus 19:18; Matthew 22:39), and one of the ways in which we can help our neighbours in the developing countries is to make more resources available for artificial contraception to married women who want it.

Genesis 1:26–31

Then God said, 'Let us make man in our image, after our likeness; and let them have dominion over the fish of the sea, and over the birds of the air, and over the cattle, and over all the earth, and over every creeping thing that creeps upon the earth.' So God created man in his own image, in the image of God he created him; male and female he created them. And God blessed them, and God said to them, 'Be fruitful and multiply, and fill the earth and subdue it; and have dominion over the fish of the sea and over the birds of the air and over every living thing that moves upon the earth.' And God said, 'Behold, I have given you every plant yielding seed which is upon the face of all the earth, and every tree with seed in its fruit; you shall have them for food. And to every beast of the earth, and to every bird of the air, and to everything that creeps on the earth, everything that has the breath of life, I have given every green plant for food.' And it was so. And God saw everything that he had made, and behold it was very good. And there was evening and there was morning, a sixth day.

Comment on the reading

This passage shows the difference between human beings and animals.

Human beings are made in the image of God: animals are not. Since we now know that humanity has evolved from the animal kingdom, we have come to realize that those characteristics of mankind which relate to the image of God are also to be found in the animal kingdom, but only in rudimentary form. These are intelligence, responsibility and the ability to make personal relationships. There still remains a huge gulf between mankind and the rest of the animal kingdom, and this is recognized in the creation story.

It is because of human intelligence that mankind has been able to gain dominion over the rest of the animal world, but this dominion, because men and women are made in the image of God, should be a responsible dominion.

It is in the context of this dominion over the animal kingdom that God, according to the creation story, orders mankind to be fruitful and multiply and to fill the earth. This command has often been gravely misunderstood, with terrible consequences. The story was written when human life was often endangered by animals and natural hazards. Human existence then was fragile, and life was often brutish and short. There was a danger that animals would get the dominion over mankind. There was a real threat to humanity that they would not be able to be fruitful and multiply. It is in this context that the command must be interpreted. It is not a licence for mankind to maximize human fertility. It is not a mandate for indefinite multiplication. It is simply a statement of God's plan for humankind, that we should have power over the animals, and that they should not restrict human fertility. The command 'fill the earth' is not the same as to overfill it. In this passage from Genesis the command to 'fill the earth' is connected with the food which God has made available for mankind (at this stage of their development people seemed to be restricted to vegetarianism). To 'fill the earth' is not a licence to increase world population to such an extent that there is no food available to feed mankind and that the natural resources of the world are endangered.

A prayer

As we face the problem of world population and feel helpless, we might make the words of Reinhold Niebuhr's prayer our own:

O God, grant us the serenity
to accept what cannot be changed,
the courage to change what can be changed
and the wisdom to know the difference.

7

The ozone layer

The sun emits very short wave ultraviolet rays, which are dangerous to human beings. Fortunately, between ten and fifty miles above the earth a gas called ozone naturally forms, which prevents these rays reaching the earth and causing a cancer known as malignant melanoma in human beings. This is the so-called ozone layer. Ozone is a gas made up of molecules of three oxygen atoms. At ground level it is dangerous to human beings, as when it forms on warm still mornings from the exhausts of motor cars. But up in the stratosphere it is literally a lifesaver. Unfortunately, if certain other gases such as chlorofluorocarbons reach the stratosphere, they release chlorine and so catalyse the destruction of ozone. This has the effect of dangerously increasing the flux of ultraviolet rays (UVB) at the earth's surface.

In the past ozone holes have only been discovered at the South and North Poles. People love sunbathing, and in Britain they have felt comparatively safe, although they have been warned to be cautious of the sun's rays and to use 'sunblockers' when sunbathing. However in late 1996 the ozone layer was found to be greatly reduced over Britain, so that it was down to summer levels. This was due to exceptional circumstances; extreme cold in the upper atmosphere. But it was worrying.

It is estimated that 1 per cent increase in UVB causes 3 per cent increase in skin cancers. Those with fair skins are more likely to be affected. UVB can also cause eye disease. It may similarly affect the immune systems of the human body, rather like the HIV virus. It can have effects too on agriculture and the marine environment. Some plant species (such as peas and beans and some forms of wheat) are sensitive to UVB radiation, which reduces their yields. It can also damage the micro-organisms in the sea which play a vital part in the oceans' food-chain.

Chlorofluorocarbon gases are man-made compounds. The story of the discovery of these gases in the atmosphere is extraordinary. When science laboratories refused his request to investigate their prevalence in the atmosphere in very small quantities, Dr James Lovelock made his own detection instrument, hitched a lift to Antarctica, and verified their existence. Later, when the news broke that CFCs were accumulating in the atmosphere, panic ensued, and vast sums were spent in stratospheric research. These failed to detect any ozone hole, because instruments were programmed to reject data that did not conform to the model that had been adopted. It was left to two British scientists, using a cheap and old-fashioned instrument, to discover the ozone hole during an Antarctic expedition.

CFCs are used for the cooling process in fridges. They are also employed for insulation purposes in buildings. They form excellent cleaners for electrical components. Fortunately their use in fridges has been phased out, but old fridges often contain them. These fridges, when they come to end of their useful lives, are often thrown out, and as the metal is recycled, the CFC gas escapes. Hydrochlorofluorocarbons (HCFCs) are also used in fridges, and as foam, as solvents and as aerosols. Other gases which similarly effect the ozone layer are carbon tetrachloride (used in chemical processes), methyl chloroform (used in metal cleaning, electronic cleaning and the manufacture of some adhesives) and halons (used in fire extinguishers). All these must be phased out worldwide.

At one point it was feared that the impact of supersonic aircraft flying high above the earth would have a bad effect on the ozone layer. Fortunately this was found to be a false alarm. Since then the number of long range aircraft which fly at high altitudes has very greatly increased. It is likely to increase still further. The effects of all these aircraft should be carefully monitored.

All these gases which affect the ozone layer must be phased out worldwide. But it is not easy for China and developing countries to do the research necessary to find substitutes. China wants a fridge for every family. This is not unreasonable. Almost every family in the West has one and who are we to say that they should hold back?

An encouraging start has been made in easing the situation. So often the story of our environment is a tale of doom and gloom. Not so with these man-made gases. Most of the nations of the world have agreed to work together to recover the ozone layer. In the Montreal Agreement they made a mutual covenant to reduce the production of anti-ozone gases. Later, in 1989, eighty-one governments signed a declaration agreeing to phase out the production and use of CFCs by the year 2000, to phase out halons as soon as possible, to restrict other ozone producing substances and to tighten up the timetable.

In doing this they promised to have special regard to the position of developing countries. The Two-Thirds-World countries did not produce the problem: the developed world did. So developed countries agreed to help in technology transfers and to assist in financing change. The countries which used the smallest amount of these gases were allowed more time.

The ozone layer will not disappear overnight. Every five-year delay in phasing out these gases results in increasing the time needed to eliminate the polar ozone holes by eighteen years. Chlorine levels, due to CFCs, are already 500 times greater than when the prevalence of CFCs in the atmosphere was first discovered twenty years ago. Even if all these gases had been phrased out by 1995, chlorine levels would not return to normal until the twenty-second century. The ozone layer is also damaged by methane gas, which is mainly the product of farming and forestry. There is another very strong reason why these gases should be phased out. They are very potent global warming gases, far stronger than carbon dioxide.

We may now compare the situation over the ozone layer with the fourth plague in chapter 16 of the book of Revelation. The two situations are very, very different. Scorching heat in Revelation is part of the punishment, according to the vision of the seer, which God will inflict on those who worship the beast instead of worshipping God. According to Revelation, they had been given due warning, but had not repented. And so the power of the sun would be released, and they would suffer terrible scorching.

Contrast this with the ozone layer. Those who used CFCs and HCFCs and the other such gases thought that they were benefiting humanity. Fridges preserve food, and prevent waste in a world already short of food. Fire is a terrible scourge which can destroy buildings and kill men and women: fire extinguishers are needed. Those who introduced these chemicals had no idea of their possible effects in the stratosphere. They acted in good faith.

God is not punishing them by making gaps in the ozone layer.

There is a moral, however. God gives us many good gifts to use in this world. But before they are used in new chemical processes, due thought should be given to their possible effects. If it becomes known that these effects are deleterious to mankind, immediate steps should be taken to rectify the situation. Those steps seem to be in the process of being taken over gaps in the ozone layer.

At the same time, before we use gases (or synthetic chemicals) we must give due thought to their possible effects. As soon as it becomes known that these will be harmful, immediate steps should be taken to stop their use. We can be grateful that steps are being taken which will eventually restore the ozone layer to what it was before the use of the gases.

Revelation 16:1–9

Then I heard a loud voice from the temple telling the seven angels, 'Go and pour out on the earth the seven bowls of the wrath of God.' So the first angel went and poured his bowl on the earth, and foul and evil sores came upon the men who bore the mark of the beast and worshipped its image. The second angel poured his bowl into the sea, and it became like the blood of a dead man, and every living thing died that was in the sea. The third angel poured his bowl into the rivers and the fountains of water, and they became blood. And I heard the angel of water say, 'Just art thou in these thy judgments, thou who art and wast, O Holy One. For men have shed the blood of saints and prophets, and thou hast given them blood to drink. It is their due!' And I heard the altar cry, 'Yea, Lord God the Almighty, true and just are thy judgments!' The fourth angel poured his bowl on the sun, and it was allowed to scorch men with fire; men were scorched by the fierce heat, and they cursed the name of God who had power over these plagues, and they did not repent and give him glory.

Comment on the reading

The book of Revelation contains a vivid account of visions given to its author to reveal the future. There are visions of many kinds, including, as here, visions of judgment, with angels blowing trumpets and pouring out bowls of wrath upon the earth. The whole purpose of these warnings and judgments was to persuade human beings to repent of the evil they were doing and to turn to God. Here the imagery is modelled on the seven plagues of Egypt, recounted in Exodus 7–12.

The fourth plague in this vision of judgment involved scorching mankind with the heat of the sun. This is not the only time in the scriptures that there is a reference to burning heat from the heavenly bodies; but elsewhere it is a description of the Last Day, when 'the heavens will pass away with a loud noise, and the elements will be dissolved with fire, and the earth and the works that are upon it will be burned up' (2 Peter 3:10). As a description of what could happen when the sun nears the end of its life and swells up to encompass the earth, it is remarkably accurate.

But in the book of Revelation the burning heat has a different purpose. Here the plagues, including the scorching sun, represent the evil which human beings bring upon themselves by turning away from God. But the increasing strength of the sun's rays, through the diminishing of the ozone layer, which we are experiencing today, is not a punishment for turning away from God. It is the result of ignorance and folly. This has resulted in interference with the natural balances which God in his providence has set up to enable us to live comfortably and comparatively safely upon earth.

For reflection

Give instruction to a wise man, and he will be still wiser: teach a righteous man and he will increase in learning.

Proverbs 9:9

We have made serious mistakes through our ignorance and folly. We may not have turned away from God deliberately; but we need wisdom before we interfere with the natural balances of creation. All wisdom ultimately comes from God, but he works through men and women, who need to take thought about the checks and balances of the natural world.

8

Nuclear power

The myriad stars which shine so bright in the sky at night are all powered by nuclear energy. All the other energy sources (coal, gas, petrol, wind, tides and so on) which we take for granted are peculiar to planet earth. Human beings tend to be frightened of nuclear power, despite its prevalence throughout the universe. This is partly because it is invisible (but so is electricity), partly because it is derived from a comparatively newly known kind of process, partly because few people understand how it is produced; and the unknown is often frightening. But it is mostly because it produces the vast explosive force of nuclear weapons which when detonated have such devastating results, and because accidents at the sites of nuclear reactors can spread deadly radiation over very large areas.

Modern hydrogen bombs are far more powerful than the atomic bombs dropped at the end of the last Great War on Hiroshima and Nagasaki. The START treaty of 1991 between the USSR and the USA has only reduced nuclear long range missiles to 7,000 on both sides. The break up of the USSR has resulted in a black market of materials used in constructing nuclear weapons. It is known that some countries are keen to have these weapons. There is a Nuclear Non-Proliferation Treaty, but not all nations have signed it. Tests of nuclear weapons by some countries are still continuing.

Nuclear weapons cannot be disinvented. The theory of nuclear power and the technology of constructing nuclear bombs and missiles are here to stay. A DIY book has actually been published on how to make a nuclear bomb! It seems that only the threat of retaliation has so far prevented their use since the end of the last Great War. Hopefully, this will continue. But, taking into account the flaws in human nature and the apparent madness of some dictators, it would not be surprising if, at some time in the future, nuclear weapons were again used in warfare. Without doubt they would inflict vast damage and kill or injure multitudes of people. Scientists have predicted a 'nuclear winter' if there were repeated exchanges of nuclear warheads. There would be darkness over the earth and normal life would come to an end. Not all the human race would inevitably perish. The effect would not be so destructive as that of a large meteorite or comet hitting the earth. But there is very good reason greatly to fear this kind of use of nuclear power.

Nuclear bombs and missiles are designed to do the maximum amount of harm. By contrast, nuclear reactors are designed to do the maximum amount of good. They are designed to generate electricity safely and under strict controls. Eighty-five per cent of the average radiation dose to UK individuals comes from natural sources (radon, gamma and cosmic rays) and through the consumption of foodstuffs which contain various naturally occurring radionuclides. Man-made sources of radiation account for the remaining 15 per cent (mostly from diagnostic X-rays). All radiation tends to cause harm (as does breathing oxygen!). The authorities have fixed a maximum permissible dose. The average individual dose in the UK is just over half of that. Less than 0.5 per cent of this comes from occupational exposure to nuclear radiation, and a further 0.1 per cent from exposure to radioactive discharges. These amounts are very, very small compared with the other sources of radiation.

Thermonuclear generation of energy presents three main types of problems. The first concerns security. Precautions must be taken against attempts to seize reactors and hold a country to ransom, and against seizure of their plutonium for nefarious ends. (In the UK there is a special nuclear security force.) Secondly, there is always the possibility of accidents with dire results. Thirdly, there is the problem of disposal of nuclear waste.

Nuclear accidents can happen through faulty design or construction, faulty operation or slackness on the part of operating staff. In 1957, in the early days of nuclear power, an accident occurred at Windscale bad enough for the authorities to change its name to Sellafield. Considerably later there was nearly a meltdown at Three Mile Island in the USA. Comparatively recently there was a partial meltdown at Chernobyl in the USSR, which has contaminated large areas of land, and caused huge numbers of casualties. It has been forecast that up to 300,000 will die of cancer as a result. I have spoken to someone who has brought relief to people in that part of the Ukraine, and he has told me that already 28,000 children have cancer, and there are many untimely or misshapen births.

Elsewhere there have been several minor discharges of radiation, and some working disorders have necessitated the temporary closedown of reactors. Some Eastern European countries are greatly dependent on nuclear energy, and so cannot afford to close down dangerous reactors. In the UK safety standards are good, and there are far less accidents, and nuclear energy is produced more safely than mining coal. After Chernobyl there has been an end, so far, to building new reactors worldwide. It is probable that sooner or later there will be more accidents, as reactors wear out. If many more reactors eventually are built, of course the risks will be proportionately greater.

When reactors do finally wear out, they have to be closed down and decommissioned. They are, of course, intensely radioactive. The process of decommissioning is extremely costly and somewhat dangerous. It was thought that uranium, the fuel of our reactors, would be in short supply, and so a 'breeder reactor economy' was planned, using reactors which produce more fuel than they consume. Fortunately this has been found unnecessary in the UK, as the dangers of this process are considerably greater. The type of reactor in use today produces nuclear wastes and material for nuclear reprocessing. There is a reprocessing plant recently in operation which takes in material from reactors overseas as well as from the UK. This radioactive material has to be transported from overseas and also from reactors in the UK. This is a potentially dangerous operation.

Nuclear wastes are of three kinds; high level, intermediate and low level. There is difficulty in the disposing of the high level wastes. They are stored for the time being in steel containers at Sellafield. An official body in Britain known as 'NIREX' has the task of arranging for their permanent disposal. Burial in the earth in deep concreted chambers is under consideration; but no one wants this in their own area. A process of reducing them to solid glass substances is said to be perfectly safe but no one can be sure what will happen to them over the next 10,000 years! It would be wrong to land posterity with this problem. For this reason we no longer dump radioactive wastes in the oceans.

It has been decided not to build any more nuclear reactors in the UK for the time being. This decision has been taken largely because energy from our thermonuclear reactors has proved very expensive. There have been long delays in construction and cost overruns; and provision has to be made for the difficult and dangerous process of eventual decommissioning. At the moment 17 per cent of power generation in the UK is from nuclear reactors.

Nuclear power has one enormous advantage over other sources of energy. It produces no carbon dioxide. Are the risks involved greater than the risks of contributing to future disasters through global overheating? That is a question over which people legitimately differ. No life is without risks of some kind. Damage to people through nuclear disaster is likely to be local (although radioactive material may be spread long distances by the winds). Global overheating, by contrast, will be worldwide and effect the future of the whole planet. Of course economies could reduce energy demand, and there could be more energy from renewable resources (which at the moment in the UK only account for 2 per cent of power generation).

At some time in the future difficult decisions will have to be made. There are still considerable reserves of gas, oil and coal. But there is no immediate prospect of fuel from nuclear fusion (which would be cheap and not so dangerous). So when the world runs of out conventional fuels for energy, it seems unlikely that alternative sources (wave power, solar power, wind power, etc.) will be able to take their place, unless the 'water fuel cell' which is being developed near Ohio in the USA can be brought into industrial production. This is claimed as a cheap means of using abstruse modern physics to abstract hydrogen from ordinary water as an immediately combustible fuel, and to produce by this means huge quantities of very cheap energy from water, of which there is of course an abundance. However, a prototype for industrial production has not yet been forthcoming. Unless and until it is it seems likely that more risks will have be taken with nuclear reactors. That is a decision that will have to be made in the twenty-first century.

2 Peter 3:8–13

> But do not ignore this one fact, beloved, that with the Lord one day is as a thousand years, and a thousand years as one day. The Lord is not slow about his promise as some count slowness, but is forbearing toward you, not wishing that any should perish, but that all should reach repentance.
>
> But the day of the Lord will come like a thief, and then the heavens will pass away with a loud noise, and the elements will be dissolved with fire, and the earth

> and the works that are upon it will be burned up.
> Since all these things are thus to be dissolved, what
> sort of persons ought you to be in lives of holiness and
> godliness, waiting for and hastening the coming of the
> day of God, because of which the heavens will be
> kindled and dissolved, and the elements will melt with
> fire! But according to his promise we wait for new
> heavens and a new earth in which righteousness
> dwells.

Comment on the reading

This passage comes from what many judge to be the latest book in the New Testament, written in the name and in the spirit of Peter rather than by the chief apostle himself. Some verses of the shorter epistle of Jude seem to have been incorporated into 2 Peter, but not the passage selected for the reading. The author is warning his readers about the end of the world, when he predicts the dissolution of both the heavens and the earth by fire, as foretold by Isaiah: 'All the host of heaven shall rot away, and the skies roll up like a scroll' (Isaiah 34:4). This will take place before the promised 'new heavens and the new earth which I will make' (Isaiah 66:22), when God's full kingdom comes, according to the biblical testimony. The Hebrew has 'new heavens' in the plural because the Jews thought of an ascending number of heavens, as when Paul wrote that he 'was caught up into the third heaven' (2 Corinthians 12:2). The author of 2 Peter introduces this theme of fire in order to warn his readers to live 'lives of holiness and godliness'. In the same way St Paul wrote to the Corinthians that the last day 'will be revealed with fire, and the fire will test what sort of work each one has done' (1 Corinthians 3:13).

Our author explains that the Lord is not delaying his coming, in the same way as the author of the epistle to the Hebrews reminds his readers that 'the coming one shall come and shall not tarry' (Hebrews 10:37, quoting the Greek translation of Isaiah 26:20). He reminds them that God's time scale is different from ours, as the Psalmist did too when he wrote: 'A thousand years in thy sight are but as yesterday... or as a watch in the night' (Psalm 90:4). There is no time in eternity, and so a day is as long as a thousand years, and a thousand years as short as a day. It may seem as if there is a delay (a thought that must have entered the head of the earliest Christians). But when the day of the Lord comes it will be quick. Like the author of 2 Peter, Paul had reminded his Thessalonian readers that 'the day of the Lord will come like a thief in the night' (1 Thessalonians 5:2). It seems likely that the phrase originated from the parable of Jesus in Matthew 24:43–44, where Jesus is reported to have said, 'If the householder had known in what part of the night the thief was coming, he would have watched and would not let his house be broken into. Therefore you also must be ready; for the Son of man is coming at an hour you do not expect.'

The prediction of the end of the world in 2 Peter is in some ways remarkably similar to the future foretold by modern cosmology. The sun will gradually use up its hydrogen as it converts it into helium. When this happens it will grow in luminosity. This will continue until the oceans boil! The sun will swell up into what is known as a 'red giant'. It will engulf the earth, and of course life will have long become extinct. This is scheduled to happen in some ten billion years' time. Yet before that long it is not unlikely that a comet or meteorite will have struck the earth, and this might happen at any time. If it is large enough it will cause so much dust that the sun will be obscured and there will be the equivalent of a 'nuclear winter' on earth, which could cause the extinction of most or even all species.

In the New Testament, the phrase 'day of the Lord' sometimes marks not (as here) the end of the world, but a coming event which marks the end of an era. In St Matthew's Gospel the coming fall of Jerusalem is regarded as a kind of 'day of the Lord', although the actual phrase is not used: 'When you see the desolating sacrilege spoken of by the prophet Daniel, standing in the holy place (let the reader understand), then let those who are in Judea flee to the mountains...' (Matthew 24:15f.). It is for this reason that this reading has been chosen as a biblical text on which to think about nuclear power. Nuclear warfare or a major disaster at a nuclear reactor are feared by many people as just such a 'day of the Lord'.

To think about

Think about Chernobyl and the damage it has done and is still doing. Think of the scorched earth of what was once one of the 'granaries of Eastern Europe'. Think of the thousands of children nearby in Ukraine who are doomed to die of cancer as a result. Think of the miscarriages and poverty of their families; and say a prayer for them.

A prayer

Grant us, Lord, grace to rejoice in life and to live each day as if it were our last.

9

Motor cars

Today everyone likes to own a motor car, if possible a fast one. Few seem to realize that a car is a lethal instrument. Some 4,500 are killed on the roads of Britain each year, and a high proportion in other European countries; and 300,000 people are injured. This is generally because cars are powerful and are driven too fast. Fast driving also wastes precious fossil fuel, and causes greater emission of polluting waste gases. There are still many people who do not have access to a motor car. Only two out of three families possess a car; and often the car is commandeered all day to get to and from work.

A car is very, very useful. It provides personalized transport. Compared with public transport, it seems cheap (although there are hidden costs). It is useful for shopping, for transporting children, for leisure and recreation, and many use the car to and from work. It is the only means of transport at times and in places where there is no public transport.

But there are other aspects of car ownership. To quote from the 1974 report of the Independent Commission on Transport:

> *There are also emotional satisfactions which a person may experience but of which he may not be conscious. For a young person the right to drive a car confers initiation into adult status. A car insulates its occupants, and especially its driver,*

from the outside world. He crawls back into his private cocoon for temporary retreat. The driver feels king of his own little universe: the people outside seem things not persons; for one part of his day he is not required to acknowledge those around him. And he can live in a fantasy world of his own making, rehearsing for his next brush with reality. He feels that he has the destiny of others in his own power, and he may exult in the mastery of man over machine. Driving can be a challenge to his manipulative and judgemental abilities, and as the car becomes an extension of his own ego, so even the slightest scratch on its bodywork can seem a person injury. The car may appear to him as a symbol of freedom, so that he may feel resentful, like an invalid, when the car is out of action. The car constitutes a symbol of both power and status, enabling a driver to confer benefits on others (such as offering a lift) and (according to the type of car that he drives) feel a member of a desirable social class. At the same time the car may enable a person to feel an equal member of a modern democratic society which has conquered space and is on the way to conquering time. It can be an outlet for aggression, giving reins to feelings of pugnacity and to the desire to prove oneself superior to others. It can also be a psychosexual outlet.

From H. Montefiore, editor, *Changing Directions*, Coronet, 1974

It is hardly surprising that the number of cars in the UK has increased enormously during the last half century until there are now over 25 million cars on the roads of Britain. It is predicted that car ownership will increase still further. The Department of Transport has predicted a maximum increase of 140 per cent during the next half century unless there are curbs. We have not got the road capacity for all these cars in this comparatively small island. More cars mean more congestion. More road building results not in easier driving but in more cars using the roads. Road enlargement results in more cars using that particular stretch of road. Until recently road building had very high priority. Millions of acres of land have been covered in tar or concrete. The beauty of the countryside is marred and scarred. Huge lorries seem out of scale, especially in towns. Roads have been favoured against railways. Since 1970 car travel per head of population has almost doubled, while travel on rail has remained static, and bus and coach use have dropped by a quarter. What is more, the real cost of motoring has fallen in real terms, and is therefore much more affordable than it was a quarter of a century ago. By contrast, the cost of rail and bus fares in real terms has increased slightly faster than the growth of disposable income.

When compared with other forms of transport, cars pollute most. Seventeen per cent of all carbon dioxide comes from burning fossil fuels, and a high proportion of this is burnt in private motor cars. Cars also produce other pollutants. Diesel, in particular, produces particulates which are inhaled and cause cancer of the lung. Lead in petrol forms dust on the road, and it is damaging, especially for small children; but fortunately there are now tax incentives to use lead-free petrol, and blood levels have fallen by a factor of almost three in adults and up to five in children. Carbon monoxide is also produced by the internal combustion engine. It disperses in the open air; but in a confined space it is lethal, and sometimes people who commit suicide choose this way inside a car. In still warm air, the exhaust gases interact with sunlight to cause ground-level ozone, which damages the lungs. These gases can also create the photochemical gases which we call smog. Sometimes the pollution is so bad that people, especially old people, are advised not to go outdoors. No one is quite certain what has caused the great increase in asthma in the UK; but pollution from car exhausts is likely to be a big contributor. Nitrogen oxides are also emitted by exhaust gases: they help to produce acid rain. Catalytic converters now have to be fitted to new cars; but old cars cannot have them fitted; and in any case the growing number of cars in use will soon make pollution worse, despite the benefit of these converters.

On these grounds alone it is in the public interest to reduce travel by private motor car, and if possible to keep more freight off the roads. This can be done in two ways; by creating disincentives to motoring, and by providing alternative means of travel and transport. Disincentives can be applied by taxation (e.g. taxing by mileage rather than by simple vehicle tax), by road pricing, by reduction in cities of public parking places and taxation of private parking, by increasing fuel taxation. We employ only the last named of these, and the effect is hard to see. Taxation is not a very fair way of reducing traffic, because it hits hardest those least able to pay.

Alternative means of travel are, for the most part, either by railway, coach, bus or bicycle. Buses have been deregulated, and the result has been more buses and fewer passengers. Coaches are cheaper than railways, but they have restricted routes and often restricted timetables. Railways emit 155 times less carbon dioxide per passenger mile than cars, but railways have been starved of investment. In the UK, in contrast to other industrialized countries, subsidies have in the past been reduced. The cost of rail travel, in contrast to the cost of motoring, has risen in proportion to the cost of living. Routes and the number of trains have been reduced. Franchising the railways is resulting in difficulties in cross-country travel in the UK. This state of affairs is unlikely to woo travellers from their motor cars to railways. The amount of freight carried by road vehicles since 1974 has increased for economic reasons, from 89 per cent of the total to 95 per cent, to the detriment of rail freight. Road freight does not pay its full share of the costs involved.

The global picture is even more depressing than the national one. Car sales in Britain are somewhat over one and a half million a year. Worldwide sales are about 50 million. In Britain there are about 25 million cars on the road.

Worldwide there are some 400 million cars in action. Older cars are likely to be more polluting. In the developing world and in China there is a great demand for cars. Why should they be available for citizens of the industrialized world, and not for those of the developing world? Why should the developed world be allowed to warm up the planet in this way, but forbid cars to the developing world? To restrict cars in the UK to those who can afford high taxation is a form of élitism: to restrict car growth to the developed world is an even worse form of élitism.

Yet cars are responsible for a great deal of global warming, and something must be done to reduce the emissions of carbon dioxide worldwide. Cars run on petrol or diesel. There is as yet no satisfactory alternative fuel which does not cause carbon dioxide pollution. Methanol, made from alcohol, is an unsatisfactory fuel in a world hungry for food. Gas, which is not transportable in large amounts, is a globe-warming fossil fuel. Electricity is mostly generated by burning coal or gas. Perhaps one day we shall have a hydrogen economy. A 'water cell' technology has already been claimed, but it is not commercially available. Until that day, cars will continue to heat up the planet.

Job 39:19–25 and Psalm 147:7–11

> 'Do you give the horse his might? Do you clothe his neck with strength? Do you make him leap like the locust? His majestic snorting is terrible. He paws in the valley, and exults in his strength; he goes out to meet the weapons. He laughs at fear, and is not dismayed; he does not turn back from the sword. Upon him rattle the quiver, the flashing spear and the javelin. With fierceness and rage he swallows the ground; he cannot stand still at the sound of the trumpet. When the trumpet sounds, he says "Aha!" He smells the battle from afar, the thunder of the captains, and the shouting'...

> Sing to the Lord with thanksgiving; make melody to our God upon the lyre! He covers the heavens with clouds, he prepares rain for the earth, he makes grass grow upon the hills. He gives to the beasts their food, and to the young ravens which cry. His delight is not in the strength of the horse, nor his pleasure in the legs of a man; but the Lord takes pleasure in those who fear him, in those who hope in his steadfast love.

Comment on the readings

Towards the end of the book of Job, after Job's friends have failed to comfort him, and he has cried out his innocence, God intervenes and speaks out of the whirlwind, and overawes him with revelations of his might from the world of nature. This passage on the horse is part of the wonders of animate nature. It is a wonderful description of a war-horse, brave, useful, strong, fearsome, beautiful and thirsting to go. In the days when the book of Job was written, the horse was a God-given means of transport, a noble animal which could gallop so very much faster than man can run and could carry loads as well as strike terror on the battlefield. Today horses are mainly used for recreation or for racing. On the battlefield the man-made mechanical tank has taken the place of the horse, and people regard their man-made and mass-produced motor cars with rather the same adulation as people in the ancient world regarded their steeds. Motor cars are thought of as swift, strong, useful, aggressive, fearsome, beautiful and thirsting to go. Instead of feeling reverence for the horse of God's creation, we transfer our adulation to the man-made internal combustion engine embodied in the modern motor car which we no longer describe in terms of 'horse power'.

The Psalmist warns us that, however wonderful qualities God has given the horse, he does not take delight in its strength or its speed, any more than he takes pleasure in the legs of a man. On the contrary, God takes delight in those who fear him and trust in his steadfast love. If that is so of the horse, how much more is it true of the motor car! This is not to deny that it is useful, swift, strong, able to carry loads, fearsome and beautiful. But it does not have intrinsic value in God's eyes: that is reserved for people through their relationships with God. The Psalmist bids us get our priorities right. Motor cars have only conditional value.

For reflection

A man on his own in a car
Is revenging himself on his wife;
He opens the throttle and bubbles with dottle
And puffs at his pitiful life.

'She's losing her looks very fast,
She loses her temper all day;
That lorry won't let me get past,
That Mini is blocking my way.

'Why can't you step on it and shift her!
I can't go on crawling like this!
At breakfast she said she wished I was dead—
Thank heavens we don't have to kiss.

'I'd like a nice blonde on my knee
And one who won't argue or nag.
Who dares to come hooting at me?
I only give way to a Jag.

'You're barmy or plastered, I'll pay you, you bastard—
I will overtake you, I will!'
As he clenches his pipe, his moment is ripe
And the corner's accepting its kill.

John Betjeman, 'Meditation on the A40'
from *High and Low*, John Murray (Publishers) Ltd

10
Global warming

Planet Earth derives all its heat from the sun (apart from what escapes through its crust from its molten core). There are complex mechanisms which have kept the climate comparatively stable for long periods. Certain gases (such as carbon dioxide and methane) rise into the atmosphere, and while the heat from the sun can pass through them, it is not so easily reflected back again into space: that is why they are called 'greenhouse gases'. Without any such 'greenhouse gases', the mean temperature on earth would be -19 degrees centigrade, 33 degrees cooler than it normally is now, and inhospitable to life. (One of the ways the earth is cooled is by the so called 'albedo effect': white reflects heat, so the whiter the surface of the earth as the result of snow and ice, the more easily its heat is reflected back into space. This explains how clouds help to cool the earth.)

The planet certainly was warm enough to support life when it first began 3.6 billion years ago despite the lesser heat of the sun then, because in those days 10 per cent of the atmosphere consisted of carbon dioxide. Since then the sun has increased in luminosity by 25 per cent, as happens with stars. (A star such as the sun produces heat by nuclear fusion, and as it begins to run out of hydrogen in its core, the star's core shrinks and gets hotter still.) Yet despite the slow increase in the heat of the sun, the temperature of the planet is more or less the same, because the carbon dioxide content of the air has reduced three hundredfold.

There is a clear relationship between the temperature of the earth and the amount of carbon dioxide in the atmosphere. In the early days carbon dioxide entered the atmosphere through chemical reactions on the earth's surface and from volcanoes. The volcanoes settled down, reducing carbon dioxide inflow, but insufficiently to account for the three hundredfold reduction in the gas. This is due to increased rainfall and the weathering of rock on the earth's surface, and also to the action of the oceans in absorbing the gas and the sinking to the ocean floor of billions of carbonate shells of micro-organisms. On land green flora photosynthesized the gas, transferring the carbon to their bodies. As the strength of the sun increased, the temperature remained stable due to a smaller 'greenhouse gas' effect. This is a highly compressed account of a complex process, which involved the alteration of an originally methane dominated atmosphere into our present oxygen dominated atmosphere.

From time to time the planet relapses into an 'ice age'. The last time this happened the mean temperature dropped by 2.5 degrees Celsius and the carbon dioxide to a mere 180 parts per million (ppm). At the start of the present warm period ('interglacial'), the temperature rose 2 degrees and carbon dioxide by another 100 ppm.

In ten years' time the carbon dioxide will have risen by almost another 100 ppm. Methane and chlorofluorocarbons (far stronger greenhouse gases than carbon dioxide) will account for the equivalent of a further 40 ppm. A rise in temperature seems inevitable. Most experts believe that it is already beginning, although others argue that recent record warm levels could be due to normal oscillations.

Carbon dioxide contributes 49 per cent of the global warming. It is caused by the combustion of the so-called 'fossil fuels' (gas, oil and coal), by deforestation (through the felling of carbon-reducing trees and the combustion of the organic material of which they consist), through changing land use and by the burning of other living organic material ('biomass'). So far as the UK is concerned, nearly a quarter of man-made production of carbon dioxide is caused by refining petrol and driving motor vehicles, 20 per cent is used in our homes (for heating and cooking), nearly a quarter goes on industry which makes the things that we buy and which produces fertilizers for farmers, and over a third is from power stations which generate electricity (coal is mostly used in them, but more gas is being burnt, and a certain proportion has now to come from alternative sources).

The initiative for reducing carbon dioxide emissions must come from the industrialized countries, for they are responsible for 90 per cent of all man-made emissions of greenhouse gases and 70 per cent of man-made carbon dioxide. The average Briton is responsible for the burning of 10.8 tonnes of fossil fuel a year, an American 18.5 tonnes, and an African 0.15 tonnes.

The UK contributes about 2 per cent to global man-made emissions of carbon dioxide (mostly through burning fossil fuels), and 1 per cent of global man-made emissions of methane (through landfill waste, gas operations and cattle flatulence). Emissions of methane are much smaller than those of carbon dioxide, but it is 25 times more powerful as a greenhouse gas. The UK also contributes 1 per cent of all nitrous oxide emissions (another greenhouse gas) from industry and agriculture. Under the impetus of the Eco-Summit of Rio de Janeiro in 1992, the UK undertook the target to return greenhouse emissions to 1990 levels by the year 2000. This target seems likely to be exceeded! Emissions of carbon dioxide relative to greenhouse gas have fallen by a fifth since 1970, although economic production in that period has increased in real terms by over 57 per cent. During this period emissions of methane gas have also fallen by 19 per cent.

Despite these reductions the future is likely to get warmer. These reductions must be only a modest start if we are restore the balance of carbon dioxide in the atmosphere. It is to the credit of the British Government that it is urging goals for the continuing reduction of carbon dioxide after the year 2000. Fortunately there is now what the Worldwatch Institute calls 'a climate of hope'. Although no new targets were set in 1996, the USA (the major polluter) agreed that regulation would be necessary. AOSIS (the Association of Small Island States, consisting of thirty-six countries fearful of being flooded if the sea level rises because of the melting of the Arctic ice-caps) is asking for a 20 per cent reduction. Support was given by the 'Group of 77' (an alliance of over a hundred developing countries). Perhaps inevitably, the oil exporting countries (e.g. Saudi Arabia and Russia) are against any regulation. But without doubt most countries are realizing that they will have to restrict carbon dioxide emissions.

It is said that the three worst enemies of the planet are the chain-saw and the motor car because of their effect on global warming, and cattle, because they need so much food to produce dairy products and meat. If we do not take urgent steps the temperature will rise by a further 3 degrees by the end of the next century, hotter than it has been for the last two million years. Already glaciers are beginning to melt in Switzerland, and some ominous cracks are appearing as the water beneath the glaciers puts pressure on rocky hillsides. Snow might melt at the poles, so that the height of the sea would rise, flooding low-lying areas of land. The oceans could rise two and a half inches every ten years, affecting two and a half million miles of coastlines. There would be changes in climate and ocean currents. The changes would be too quick for natural vegetation and crops to adapt. Agriculture and natural ecosystems would be badly affected. These ecosystems are very flexible; but, like elastic, when stretched too far, they snap. One disaster could lead to another. For example if snow melted at the poles, there would be less 'albedo effect' to reflect heat back into space, escalating the greenhouse effect.

However there is much about natural climate regulation that we do not know. When it is warm, much more water vapour can exist in the air. This could bring about high cloud which can reflect back heat before it reaches the earth. The oceans can store heat better than the land, so some could be absorbed that way. Warming the polar regions, if this did not melt the ice, could have the effect of producing more water vapour and so more snow. Living micro-organisms could also help to regulate the warming climate. There is much we do not yet know.

But we do know enough to realize that we are likely to have an unstable climate in the foreseeable future. A sudden jump in climate of 2.5 degrees may well produce unpleasant surprises, whether it jolts the earth into another ice age or whether it forces the planet to settle into a future state of heat that is inhospitable to mankind. The oscillation of interglacials and ice ages over the last two million years suggests the development of some structural instability in climate regulation. Large emissions of man-made greenhouse gases could give the system the coup de grâce.

What can be done? Unless the as yet unproved 'water fuel cell' can produce energy from water (which would not involve the production of greenhouse gases), a complete change of attitude will be required. This is the more difficult to achieve because developing nations naturally want to catch up with industrial nations, and are likely to produce more greenhouse gases as they try to do so; and everyone seems to want more of everything. (One fifth of the world—the developed world—uses four-fifths of the world's resources.) Nations must develop much larger supplies of renewable energy. The sum of individual choices can make a huge difference. Driving private motor cars must give way to greater use of public transport. Kettles should be boiled half full. Houses should be insulated so that they need less heat. Long life light bulbs should be used. Washing machines should only be used on full load. More gas is used in cracked pipes than is burnt! The list of economies could be continued at length. At the moment there seems little feeling of urgency and little encouragement to economize. Privatized energy companies are competing to sell us not less but more energy.

Psalm 19:1–10

The heavens are telling the glory of God; and the firmament proclaims his handiwork. Day to day pours forth speech, and night to night declares knowledge. There is no speech, nor are there words; their voice is not heard; yet their voice goes out through all the earth, and their words to the end of the world.
In them he has set a tent for the sun, which comes forth like a bridegroom leaving his chamber, and like a strong man runs its course with joy. Its riding is from the end of the heavens, and its circuit is to the end of them; and there is nothing hid from its heat.

The law of the Lord is perfect, reviving the soul; the testimony of the Lord is sure, making wise the simple; the precepts of the Lord are right, rejoicing the heart; the commandment of the Lord is pure, enlightening the eyes; the fear of the Lord is clean, enduring for ever; the ordinances of the Lord are true, and righteous altogether. More to be desired are they than gold, even much fine gold; sweeter also than honey and drippings of the honeycomb.

Comment on the reading

This passage comes from one of a collection of fifty-four psalms in our Psalter, all described as 'For David'. These probably comprised an early Psalter, later incorporated into the Great Psalter which is part of our Bible. This psalm, like fifty-seven others, is prefaced by the word 'Mizmur', which indicates a further collection. It is also ascribed to the 'Director' a word only found elsewhere in the book of Chronicles, and this indicates its use in early synagogue worship. It has been suggested that the first two stanzas of the psalm, in praise of nature and in particular of the sun, originally stood on its own: so also did the remainder of the psalm, which is in praise of the Law, and which has a different poetic form. If this is the case, the two were combined to show the coherence and compatibility of the natural law and the revealed Law of Moses.

'The heavens', 'the firmament', 'day' and 'night' are all personified as we may expect in poetic diction. The author is concerned here not with the earth, but the heavenly bodies. Their very existence is a manifestation of God's glory and can only be ascribed to the handiwork of God, as in Psalm 8:3 where it is described as 'the work of thy fingers'. The firmament is the whole expanse of heaven. It is conceived here somewhat differently from Genesis 1:7 where we are simply told 'God made the firmament'. Here it is conceived as being spread out by the hands of God at the creation. Isaiah too speaks of 'God, the Lord, who created the heavens and stretched them out' (Isaiah 42:5) and 'I am the Lord, who made all things, who stretched out the heavens alone' (Isaiah 44:24). Night and day make known the glory of God in an endless chain of praise rather like two parts of a choir chanting alternately the praises of God, except of course that their praise is wordless.

The second stanza is in parallel to the first. Whereas the first stanza is in praise of God, the second does not mention God but is in praise of the sun. This has suggested to some that originally this was a hymn to the sun god Shemesh, who was worshipped in Jerusalem just before the exile (Ezekiel 8:16), and that it was later 'baptized' into monotheistic Judaism. Others have supposed that it was specifically composed against pagan sun worship. More probably the sun here represents God, as we find in Psalm 84:11: 'The Lord God is a sun and shield'. The imagery is poetic. During the night the sun has been resting in his tent. In Habakkuk 3:11 sun and moon share a dwelling: they 'stood still in their habitation'. But the imagery used here ('as a bridegroom') does not imply that the sun was married. It suggests rather that he begins his daily journey from east to west with all the vigour of a young man refreshed by sleep. In the days when the psalm was written, the sun was thought to move round a flat earth, rather than the globe of the earth to revolve round the sun. So the sun makes its circuit from one end of heaven to the other. Nothing can escape its heat. This was a cause for rejoicing when the psalm was written. Today, as we warm up the planet, it gives us cause for some alarm.

A promise to the ancient Jews and a prayer for ourselves:

I lift up my eyes to the hills.
  From whence does my help come?
My help comes from the Lord,
  who made heaven and earth.
He will not let your foot be moved,
  he who keeps you will not slumber.
Behold, he who keeps Israel
  will neither slumber nor sleep.
The Lord is your keeper;
  the Lord is your shade on your right hand.
The sun shall not smite you by day,
  nor the moon by night.
The Lord will keep you from all evil;
  he will keep your life.
The Lord will keep your going out
  and your coming in
  from this time on and for evermore.

Psalm 121

11
Acid rain

Acid rain is the name commonly given to acid deposition, whether by rain or by mist or in dry form. It is the term given to the various processes by which man-made emissions of sulphur dioxide and nitrogen oxide and ammonia are deposited on land and water, often at long distances from the source of the pollution—70 per cent from sulphur dioxide and 30 per cent from nitrogen oxide.

However, 40 per cent of all acid rain occurs naturally. Ever since oxygen became the dominant gas in our atmosphere, all rain has been acid. Britain is often blamed for the sterile lakes and rivers of Scandinavia; but in fact nearly half of the cause originates from micro-organisms in the surface of the Atlantic Ocean and the seas around Sweden. Only some 15 per cent is the result of industrial pollution from Britain blown over the North Sea. Dimethyl sulphide is produced by marine algae and produces the nuclei around which rain clouds can form over the oceans; and emissions from the seas round Scandinavia are probably rising owing to nutrients washed down into the North Sea from agricultural fertilizers causing 'eutrophication', that is, a state in which nutrients from fertilizers cause excessive algae and plant growth which uses up the oxygen in the water, causing the death of marine life. As for nitric acids, they are produced by lightning and fires, and the natural carbon dioxide in the atmosphere causes carbonic acid. Hence the presence of acid in all rainfall.

Whilst 40 per cent of acid rain occurs naturally, the remaining 60 per cent is man-made. It is this that causes damage. The damage is measured by the exceeding of 'the critical load', which is the estimated level of deposition below which present knowledge indicates that there are no significant harmful effects on a specified sensitive area of the environment. The area of Britain where sulphur deposition exceeded the critical load of acidity for soils decreased from 38 per cent over the period 1986/8 to 32 per cent in 1989/92. This indicates that one third of the area of land soils in Britain is subject to some damage. The area where the deposition was over twice the critical load has also fallen during this period from 11 per cent to 9 per cent. This indicates that one tenth of the land soil area of Britain is badly affected. As for fresh waters (that is, non-salt waters), the critical loads have remained unchanged at around 17 per cent since the mid 1980s.

As for soil pollution, acid rain can inhibit plant nutrition and restrict the range of both flora and fauna. Pollution can affect trees. It can happen quite quickly. Between 1982 and 1983, 40 per cent of the forest area of Germany seems to have been affected. Once deposition has passed a critical level, damage takes place rapidly. In Britain a survey in 1989 showed that 28 per cent of the trees surveyed had moderate to severe defoliation. I could hardly believe this, until I began examining trees in Wales, and found that their tops were not growing properly.

As for pollution in fresh waters, these areas can become toxic to aquatic plants, invertebrates and fish. There are rivers in England and Wales which no longer support fish as a result of this pollution. The most vulnerable soils are to be found in the upland areas of north and west Britain. The snails and invertebrates which the fish eat cannot survive, the fish eggs cannot hatch and the fry are killed. The fish themselves may be killed by the acidity of the water, or they may suffocate because their gills become clogged through the concentration of aluminium which is permitted by the acidity of the water. Rivers in western and central Scotland, the Lake

District, the Pennines and the Welsh uplands are now affected.

Acid rain also affects buildings. Why have so many of our listed buildings and ancient cathedrals been in need of restoration this century? Mostly because of the deterioration caused by acid rain. A report in 1990 suggested that building maintenance work could be substantially reduced if there were a 30 per cent reduction in ambient sulphur dioxide levels. It was also suggested that the cost of this reduction would be less than the cost of the building maintenance work made necessary by this pollution.

Acid rain also affects human beings. Sulphur and nitrogen compounds can result in breathing problems. Ozone at ground level (which also retards the growing crops) is formed through the interaction of sunlight and nitrogen oxides. When conditions are very bad old people may be advised to stay at home. Newspapers nowadays tend to publish in addition to weather forecasts information about probable sulphur and nitrogen levels; and cyclists often wear masks. Levels sometimes exceed the guidelines laid down by the World Health Organization.

What are the specific causes of acid rain? Seventy-one per cent of man-made pollution of sulphur dioxide comes from power stations generating electricity; and the rest from industry. The UK story of gradual reductions is an unhappy one. In 1985 the UK refused to join the Helsinki Protocol for a 30 per cent reduction in sulphur dioxide emissions. In 1984 the European Community finally agreed an air directive after a delay of five years, largely due to UK objections. Even then different countries agreed on differing limitations to emissions. The UK obtained relatively undemanding limits on the understanding that Flue Gas Desulphurization devices be fitted to six of the large power stations. The UK later reneged on this, and only three were fitted. It was left to privatized power companies to use natural gas or to fit their own devices. (The European Community also insisted that by 1992 all new cars would be fitted with catalytic converters.) In

1984 the UK agreed that between 1980 and 1993 sulphur dioxide emissions would be reduced by 20 per cent, and by 60 per cent by 2003. As we have already noted above, soil pollution has only dropped by small amounts in the 1980s, and pollution in fresh waters has not decreased at all; so it seems that this agreement also will not be honoured. However, very recently the two largest electricity producers have been ordered to cut emissions of sulphur by 85 per cent by the year 2005.

As for nitric acids, in 1988 Britain refused to join with twelve other countries in an informal 30 per cent 'nitrogen oxide club'. The most it would do was to join the Sofia Protocol, which agreed to a standstill by 1994 in nitrogen oxide emissions at a 1987 baseline. Road transport accounts for nearly a half, power stations for a third, and the rest comes from industry. The UK had agreed in 1984 for progressive reductions in the levels of man-made emissions of nitrogen oxides. No statistics however have been issued: it is merely stated that 'in future it should be possible to produce indicators for soils at critical load exceedencies once methodologies have received international approval'. In other words, we can't even find out at present what is happening; a very unsatisfactory state of affairs.

While the gases mentioned above form acid rain, there are other atmospheric pollutants which must be mentioned. The 1991 Report of the Organization for Economic Cooperation and Development (of the G7 countries) contains the following: 'More and more toxic pollutants (e.g., cadmium, benzine, radon, asbestos) are being released into the atmosphere. Even though they are emitted in smaller quantities than traditional air pollutants, they may have equal or greater impacts on the natural environment and human health: many of them are carcinogenic or cause other long-term irreversible toxic effects. The combined intake of several of these toxic trace pollutants, not only from air but also through food and drinking water, may exert an even greater effect than that of any of them taken singly. Available evidence shows that indoor air may be of considerable lower quality in many instances than outdoor air, and people may be exposed to much higher levels of traditional and toxic air pollutants than was originally believed, since they spend about 90 per cent of their time in buildings or vehicles.'

Genesis 19:15–26

When morning dawned, the angels urged Lot, saying, 'Arise, take your wife and your two daughters who are here, lest you be consumed in the punishment of the city.' But he lingered; so the men seized him and his wife and his two daughters by the hand, the Lord being merciful to him, and they brought him forth and set him outside the city. And when they had brought them forth, they said, 'Flee for your life; do not look back or stop anywhere in the valley; flee to the hills, lest you be consumed.' And Lot said to them, 'Oh, no, my lords; behold, your servant has found favour in your sight, and you have shown me great kindness in saving my life; but I cannot flee to the hills, lest the disaster overtake me, and I die. Behold, yonder city is near enough to flee to, and it is a little one. Let me escape there—is it not a little one?—and my life will be saved!' He said to him, 'Behold, I grant you this favour also, that I will not overthrow the city of which you have spoken. Make haste, escape there; for I can do nothing till you arrive there.' Therefore the name of the city was called Zoar. The sun had risen on the earth when Lot came to Zoar.

Then the Lord rained on Sodom and Gomorrah brimstone and fire from the Lord out of heaven; and he overthrew those cities, and all the valley, and all the inhabitants of the cities, and what grew on the ground. But Lot's wife behind him looked back, and she became a pillar of salt.

Comment on the reading

There is no passage in the Bible that contains a reference to acid rain, but this is probably the nearest equivalent. It is very likely that there was an huge explosion in the time of Abraham which wiped out these two cities in the Rift Valley through which the Jordan flows; and probably Lot, Abraham's nephew, and his family just managed to make good their escape. The connection of this destruction with the two towns of Sodom and Gomorrah and the nature of their wickedness is uncertain.

Sodom and Gomorrah are mentioned elsewhere in the scriptures. In Isaiah 1:10–20 their sin is insincere worship and injustice and oppression. The prophet said: 'Hear the word of the Lord, you rulers of Sodom! Give ear to the teaching of our God, you people of Gomorrah! What is to me the multitude of your sacrifices, says the Lord?' But according to Jeremiah 23:14 it is adultery and lying: 'In the prophets of Jerusalem I have seen a horrible thing: they commit adultery and walk in lies... all of them have become like Sodom to me, and its inhabitants like Gomorrah'. On the other hand Ezekiel put down their sin to haughtiness and unwillingness to help those in need: 'Behold, this was the guilt of your sister Sodom: she and her daughters had pride, surfeit of food and prosperous ease, but did not aid the poor and needy' (Ezekiel 16:49). In Ecclesiasticus their sin is put down to arrogance: 'He did not spare the neighbours of Lord' (Ecclesiasticus 16:8), while according to the Wisdom of Solomon it was all about hospitality. They 'practised a more bitter hatred of strangers. Others had refused to receive strangers when they came to them but these made slaves of guests who were their benefactors' (Wisdom of Solomon 19:13f.) Clearly Sodom and Gomorrah in the Old Testament were regarded as a sink of every kind of iniquity! Here in Genesis 19 their sins were not only inhospitality but also (according to the usual interpretation) homosexual gang rape. Whatever may have been thought to be the cause behind the destruction of the two cities, this reading has been chosen for a different reason.

It has been selected because acid rain would have been among the debris which rained down on the Jordan valley. Most probably a tectonic earthquake left fissures through which compressed inflammable gases escaped, together with petroleum, lying at a considerable depth below the surface. These readily ignited, through a flash of lightning or spontaneously, and then there rained down burning showers of debris, while a dense smoke pall hung in the air. (Such a happening occurred in Canada when a borehole struck a reservoir of condensed gas which ignited with petroleum, and an area of fifteen acres soon was engulfed in flames.) Hydrogen sulphide would have been among the gases, for even today there are sulphur springs and sulphur deposits in the bituminous soil around the Dead Sea, as well as bituminous matter. Sulphur gases are one of the causes of acid rain; and so among other horrors acid rain would have destroyed vegetation and fish in the area of the explosion. Such events are called by insurance companies 'acts of God', because there seems no human cause for them. But, as we have seen, it seems that there is a human cause for 60 per cent of our acid rain.

Think and pray about acid rain

Ask rain from the Lord in the season of the spring
rain,
from the Lord who makes the storm clouds,
who gives men showers of rain,
to every one the vegetation in the field.

Zechariah 10:1

Think about rain that is pure and unpolluted, which falls upon the ground and which the trees and plants draw up from their roots. Then think about acid rain, dilute sulphuric acid burning the tender shoots of the trees and finally killing them. Think of the barren rivers and lakes. Think about the way in which we misuse God's gifts. Pray for the will and the wisdom for these things to be put right, and to put ourselves right.

12

Agriculture

The bulging display counters of supermarkets suggest that there is food in abundance. The existence of 'set aside' land on our farms confirms this impression. But it is no longer the case. The grain mountains of the Common Market have disappeared. There are only forty-eight days reserve supplies of cereal in the world. Only 1 billion in the world out of 5.5 billion are well fed today. Long-term shortages and even famines seem probable in the future.

We had been told that advances of the 'Green Revolution' would put an end to such fears. But there are 90 million more mouths to feed every year, and for the last three years the total cereal harvest has actually declined to what are virtually only pipeline supplies. In 1994 China exported 8 million tons of grain: in 1995 she imported 16 million. (One quarter of all grain that is produced does not directly feed people, but cattle.) Under such circumstances prices mount steeply; and they have.

Crops of grain or rice depend on well-fertilized soil, sufficient acreage to sow, the right seeds, good weather, enough supplies of water. As for the weather, the probability of future climate change will endanger future harvests. As for seed production, there have certainly been spectacular advances due to plant research. But although the new seeds produce so plentifully, their crops do not contain the same mix of necessary trace minerals that their predecessors had. There is much standardization. But variety is necessary, for future changing conditions may require different kinds of seeds for the maximum return. Monocultures encourage the growth of pests by providing ideal conditions for their development.

As for acreage, the world reached an all-time high of 732 million hectares in 1981. (A hectare is nearly 2.5 acres.) By 1995 this had declined to 699 million hectares. The difference is mainly due to the loss of badly eroded land in the former USSR, the increasing industrialization of Asia, and the conversion of erodible cropland back to grass in the USA. As for soil quality, in many parts of the world this has declined due to overuse and erosion. Soil structure may be damaged by heavy machinery. The constituents of and impurities in natural and chemical fertilizer, such as heavy metals, can accumulate in the soil. Copper, added to pig feed to encourage growth, can be found in pig slurry and spread over the ground. Cadmium can accumulate when inorganic phosphates or sewage sludge is applied. Metals are hard to eliminate from the soil, and they can lead to reduced soil fertility. Excessive concentrations can find their way into the crops cultivated. Happily, research shows that in the UK over the last quarter century soil quality has not changed appreciably.

Farming accounts for 70 per cent of all fresh water use on the planet! From 1950 to 1978, the irrigated area of the world increased nearly 3 per cent a year, from 94 to 206 million hectares. This raised the irrigated area per person by 28 per cent. After 1978 growth was scarcely 1 per cent a year. Since 1990 there has been no growth at all. It will not be easy to increase it. Many aquifers are running low, in many cases because of the increasing scale of water abstraction from rivers. Many rivers are running drier: droughts have a more immediate effect. Deforestation and soil erosion causes silting of reservoirs. Water tends to be diverted from irrigation for agriculture to non-farm use. In some areas injudicious use of irrigation has raised salts to the surface, making the soil less fertile.

The prodigal use of antibiotics is resulting in new strains

of bacteria developing multi-drug resistance, and attention has been drawn to the danger of a future health crisis. Antibiotics are frequently administered to farmyard animals as a preventive medicine; and it is thought that this tends to assist the trend towards resistance.

As for artificial fertilizers, their use was boosted from 1950 to 1989 from 14 million to 146 million tons. This was the main reason why the grain harvest increased threefold during this period. Since 1989 fertilizer use has actually declined. Existing crop varieties cannot effectively use more fertilizer than is at present applied. In any case the use of these fertilizers causes problems, and in the long term the soil is left less fertile than when the artificial fertilizers were first applied. The phenomenal increase in world tonnage of crops to keep pace with the rising world population was to a great extent due to the application of artificial fertilizer. But the old formula no longer works, and scientists have not come up with a new one.

The ploughing up of grassland releases large quantities of nitrates into the environment. The intensive use of nitrogen fertilizers can cause large quantities of nitrates to leach into the ground water. This can cause problems over a certain threshold. Problems can also be caused by surface spreading of animal manure or slurry. In England and Wales about 5 per cent of the land is found to be a 'nitrate sensitive zone', where strict controls will be made on the amount of manure which may be spread or slurry applied. Above 50 milligrams a litre, nitrates can cause 'blue baby' syndrome and stomach cancer. Phosphates and nitrates, applied as artificial fertilizer, can not only find their way into the ground water: they may also run off into rivers and find their way to estuaries, where they can cause 'eutrophication' of algae, with adverse effects on fish.

Pesticides are an important aid to agriculture. Unfortunately some pests develop a resistance to pesticides. Non-specific pesticides may eliminate benign species such as pollinating insects. Organophosphates need very careful handling by humans and are toxic. Fungicides generally are toxic for fish.

The presence of trace elements of pesticides as well as heavy metals in foodstuffs is a matter of increasing public concern, despite claims that no safety levels have been breached. Nonetheless it is advised that carrots be peeled before consumption. There are those who prefer organic farming methods, using only natural fertilizer. Many consumers prefer these products. However, if such methods were introduced worldwide, there would be an acute food shortage of cereals.

One thousand new chemical substances reach the market annually. Hormonally active synthetic chemicals are widely used in agriculture. Some of these are long lasting and have become pervasive throughout the environment. In the past they have mostly been tested simply against cancer. But there is now growing evidence that they can cause damage that is passed on to the next generation if they are exposed to them during the short period in which their reproductive system is laid down in the embryo. There are subtle connections between the endocrine system of the body (which controls sexuality and much else), the immune system and the intelligence. Even a few parts per trillion of some synthetic chemicals (that is, a million times a million time a million) have been shown to have adverse results. These chemicals can build up in the food chain. 'Animals contaminated by these chemicals show various behavioural effects, including aberrant mating behaviour and increased parental neglect of nests. Synthetic chemicals can derail the normal expression of sexual characteristics of animals, in some cases masculinizing females and feminizing males. Some animal studies indicate that exposure to hormonally active chemicals prenatally or in adulthood increases vulnerability to hormone-responsive cancers, such as malignancies in the breast, prostate, ovary and uterus' (T. Colbourn and others, *Our Stolen Future*,

Little, Brown, 1996). There is no proof that hormonally active synthetic chemicals affect humans, although diminished sperm counts and increases in testicular and breast cancers and possibly in behavioural disorders give rise to suspicions.

The vast acreage now cleared for arable land brings wider problems. For example rice paddies are a potent source of methane gas, which is itself a strong 'greenhouse' gas. The cutting down of forests to produce arable land contributes to climate change and alteration of weather patterns.

One of the effects of using land for arable purposes is the loss of natural flora and fauna. Wild plants are killed by ploughing and pesticides. Wild animals and birds lose their habitats. Species are put at risk worldwide. As an example, the effects of farming on birds in the UK may be cited. Ten years ago there were only eight species on the 'red list'. Today there are thirty-six. Twenty-three of these have had their populations halved during the last quarter century. On the present list nine species of birds have been added—the turtle dove, the skylark, song thrush, spotted flycatcher, tree sparrow, linnet, bullfinch, reed bunting, and corn bunting. These all used to be common country birds. The causes of their scarcity are thought to be the change from spring- to winter-sown cereals, neglect and grubbing out of hedgerows and the use of pesticides. (Some of our birds have become extremely rare. The red-backed shrike raises no young in Britain at all, and the linnet and the skylark have deceased in population by a half over the last twenty years.) The drying out of wetlands for arable production reduces wading birds by denying them their accustomed habitat.

Christians will be aware that there are important moral questions here. What right have we to permit the use of synthetic chemicals which can affect future generations, simply in order to produce more and cheaper foodstuffs? What right have we to endanger whole species of animals? Public opinion can do a great deal to enforce change in these matters.

Deuteronomy 8:7–14, 17–20

For the Lord your God is bringing you into a good land, a land of brooks of water, of fountains and springs, flowing forth in valleys and hills, a land of wheat and barley, of vines and fig trees and pomegranates, a land of olive trees and honey, a land in which you will eat bread without scarcity, in which you will lack nothing, a land whose stones are iron, and out of whose hills you can dig copper. And you shall eat and be full, and you shall bless the Lord your God for the good land he has given you.

Take heed lest you forget the Lord your God, by not keeping his commandments and his ordinances... which I command you this day: lest, when you have eaten and are full... and when your herds and flocks multiply, and your silver and gold is multiplied, and all that you have is multiplied, then your heart be lifted up, and you forget the Lord your God...

Beware lest you say in your heart, 'My power and the might of my hand hath gotten me this wealth.' You shall remember the Lord your God, for it is he who gives you power to get wealth; that he may confirm his covenant which he swore to your fathers, as at this day. And if you forget the Lord your God and go after other gods and serve them and worship them, I solemnly warn you this day that you shall surely perish. Like the nations that the Lord makes to perish before you, so shall you perish, because you would not obey the voice of the Lord your God.

Comment on the reading

This passage in Deuteronomy is an exhortation against idolatry and self-glorification. It is addressed to people who, after overcoming great privations and trials during forty years of wandering, have triumphantly entered into the Promised Land. But in fact the author wrote much later than that. He was addressing a people who had long entered into their inheritance. In other words, he was using the past as a warning against present temptations.

The contents of the reading are extraordinarily relevant to the present day. Increasing affluence and a desire for better living conditions and a higher standard of living have tempted many to ignore the commandments of God. Idolatry, or the setting up of other gods, such as possessions or money, are greater today than they were when the author wrote these words. The temptation of self-deification has increased through the power of technology. People really think that their improved conditions are purely the result of their own doing rather than dependent on the gift of God, for many think that man is the measure of all things.

The commandments and covenant mentioned here refer to the Israelites and their duty to keep the Law of Moses. But they also apply universally to everyone who is disobedient to the natural law. In the attempt to get out of nature more than it can properly provide, we are bringing famine and ruin upon ourselves. No longer are rivers and springs full of water: no longer is there abundance of food for the human race. The multiplication of herds and flocks is causing erosion of the soil. Fertilizers bring only short-term benefits, and pesticides may cause lethal side-effects. There is a natural law set by God by which the land is kept serviceable. We ignore this at our peril.

To think about

The earth mourns and withers,
the world languishes and withers;
the heavens languish together with the earth.
The earth lies polluted under its inhabitants;
for they have transgressed the laws,
violated the statutes,
broken the everlasting covenant.

Isaiah 24:4–5

13
Cattle

BSE has been heralded as an unmitigated disaster. It is certainly disastrous for many British farmers who breed cattle or keep dairy herds, for they are likely to lose much money and perhaps even their livelihood. But would it be a disaster for the planet if large numbers of cattle were to be culled? Would it be seen as if the dream of Pharaoh in the Bible reading had come true, and that lean and gaunt cows, or at any rate staggering cows, have engulfed the rest of the national cattle herd? No one as yet has examined the ecological background to the BSE epidemic.

Domesticated animals now outnumber the human race by a ratio of three to one. There are 2 billion four-legged livestock and 11 billion fowls. Within forty years meat production has quadrupled. Whether this has improved the health of the human race may be doubted; but it has certainly not improved the health of the planet. It has been observed that 'an alien ecologist, observing the earth, might conclude that cattle is the dominant animal species in our biosphere'. Cattle and other livestock such as pigs and poultry graze one-half of the planet's total land area. This has had large impacts on the ecology of the earth.

Before cattle were bred intensively for human consumption, and before the era of massive artificial fertilizers for crops, cattle formed part of the rotation of land use which kept it fertile. Cattle in more primitive days had a large variety of uses: transport, manure both for fuel and for natural fertilizers and clothing. In earlier days, domesticated animals turned what people could not eat into what they could eat; cattle and sheep ate grass, and pigs and fowl ate kitchen scraps and crop wastes and anything else they could find. Not so today. Cattle in the industrialized countries are fed grain, and a quarter of the grain harvest is consumed by them; this, at a time of predicted crop shortages and increasing costs of grain. Domesticated animals produce so much manure that in some countries it is difficult to find anywhere to store it, let alone use it; and special legislation has had to be introduced on this account by the European Union to safeguard human health.

There are actually more cattle at any one time in developing countries than in the developed countries. This is because they live longer. In the industrialized countries the production of beef cattle is four times as large, but they are killed off much earlier, being fed on grain and putting on weight much more quickly. Often in undeveloped countries the people are pastoralists. Pressures of population have forced people to put on the land more cattle than it can properly support, and the result is soil erosion. It has already been noted that much forest has been cut down in order to produce more grazing land. Within twenty years, twenty million hectares of forest have been cut down for farms and ranches, especially in Brazil, Bolivia and Columbia. In fact such land is of very poor quality, and cannot support livestock for long. In countries where there is overgrazing, the cattle eat the perennial grasses, so weeds and tougher shrubs spread in their place. Cattle tend to stamp down the soil, which can become impermeable to rain. When it does rain, the topsoil tends to be swept away and deep gullies formed. In countries such as Botswana deep bore holes have to be dug to provide water for cattle. The cattle are not controlled around these bore holes, which tend to become bare and infertile. This is part of the process of 'desertification' which has already affected a third of the world's 3 billion hectares of dry rangeland.

Here is the verdict of the highly respected Worldwatch Institute in Washington:

> *Rings of barren earth spread out from the wells on the grasslands of southern Turkmenia. Heather and lilies wilt in the nature preserves of the southern Netherlands. Forests teeming with rare forms of life explode in flame in Costa Rica. Water tables fall and fossil fuels are wasted in the United States. Each of these cases of environmental decline issues from a single source, the global livestock industry.*

There are hidden costs in intensive beef production. All farm animals that are fed intensively are given grain. As we have noted, one quarter of all grain produced cannot be consumed by hungry people, but is fed to animals which only the rich can afford to buy. Furthermore, it is energy-consuming. The grain is grown with the use of artificial fertilizer, which costs much energy to produce. (In American pig production, it takes the equivalent of four litres of petrol to produce two pounds of pork.)

In developed countries with intensive farming, wastes from cattle tend to degrade the soil. In the Netherlands and elsewhere more phosphorus and nitrogen is produced than the soil can properly absorb. Nitrogen from manure escapes into the air as ammonia, and so contributes to acid rain. In some areas, pollution from cattle contributes more to acid rain than does industrial pollution. There is an even graver pollutant: methane. We have already noted that as a greenhouse gas it is twenty-five times more potent than carbon dioxide. Cattle emit some 80 million tons of methane gas into the atmosphere each year in belches and flatulence, and a further 35 million tons is produced from their wastes. Livestock account for between 15 and 20 per cent of global emissions of methane gas, which works out at 3 per cent of all greenhouse gases.

As with crops, so with livestock. The cutting down of forest lands, the alteration of use from wild to cultivated land of huge areas of the world in the long run will create changes in climate and temperature which will be felt far beyond the areas concerned. This is probably the most serious aspect of cattle production.

Consumption of meat greatly varies in different parts of the world. At the moment, meat consumption in the USA runs at 112 kilograms per person a year. In India it is only 2 kilograms (and, of course, none of that is beef, for the cow is sacred). Eastern Europe has a tradition of high meat consumption. The European Union consumes an average of 72 kilograms per person. Beef consumption in the UK has dropped since the BSE scare, but has since returned to within 20 per cent of normal.

The problems are partly the increasing numbers of human population, partly the demand for a higher standard of living by those living in the developed world. It would be impossible to raise the meat consumption of the developing countries so that it reaches that of the developed countries. The present size of the global herd of livestock and the present numbers of domesticated animals is unsustainable. If the BSE scare changes permanently the eating habits of the developed countries it would be no bad thing, ecologically speaking; and farmers would then have to adapt to the production of food less damaging to the environment.

Genesis 41:9–21

Then the chief butler said to Pharaoh, 'I remember my faults today. When Pharaoh was angry with his servants, and put me and the chief baker in custody in the house of the captain of the guard, we dreamed on the same night, he and I, each having a dream with its own meaning. A young Hebrew was there with us, a servant of the captain of the guard; and when we told him, he interpreted our dreams for us, giving an interpretation to each man according to his dream.

And as he interpreted to us, so it came to pass; I was restored to my office, and the baker was hanged.' Then Pharaoh sent and called Joseph, and they brought him hastily out of the dungeon; and when he had shaved himself, and changed his clothes, he came in before Pharaoh. And Pharaoh said to Joseph, 'I have had a dream, and there is no one who can interpret it; and I have heard it said of you that when you hear a dream, you can interpret it.' Joseph answered Pharaoh, 'It is not in me; God will give Pharaoh a favourable answer.' Then Pharaoh said to Joseph, 'Behold in my dream I was standing on the banks of the Nile; and seven cows, fat and sleek, came up out of the Nile and fed in the reed grass; and seven other cows came up after them, poor and very gaunt and thin, such as I had never seen in all the land of Egypt. And the thin and gaunt cows ate up the seven fat cows, but when they had eaten them no one would have known they had eaten them, for they were still as gaunt as at the beginning. Then I awoke...'

Comment on the reading

The style of the Joseph stories in Genesis is unlike that of the accounts of the other earlier Jewish patriarchs. Whatever its historical basis, the account of Pharaoh's dream, and its part in the release of Joseph from an unfair imprisonment, is vividly told. Like Daniel, Joseph found royal favour by his God-given gift for interpreting royal dreams (Daniel 4), and is given pride of place by the king. There were two dreams, not dissimilar; only the first dream is recounted in this reading. It does not, with hindsight, appear very difficult to interpret; and it is surprising that the Egyptian wise men and magicians were unable to make any sense out of it. The seven fat cows represented seven years of plenty, and they were followed by seven lean cows, which represented seven years of famine; and when the lean cows ate up the fat cows without appearing in any way to be fattened by this diet, this represented the possibility that all the bounty of the first seven years of plenty would be swallowed up by the famine which would follow it.

The story makes it clear that this was only a dream. According to the story, the reality lay in the prophecy of years of plenty throughout the ancient world, followed by years of famine. So the dream is not directly applicable to the situation today. Nonetheless it does suggest certain similarities. In the latter part of the twentieth century there have been apparent years of plenty: will these be followed by years of famine, in which all the good done by the years of plenty will be undone? Will thin and gaunt cattle be the undoing of the good healthy cattle? Certainly there seems a chance that in the interests of allaying public confidence about BSE and CJD diseases, many good healthy cattle may be sacrificed because of the few mad cows suffering from BSE. But there is an even larger question which must be raised. Will the existence of the billion cattle which at present exist on earth, most of them healthy and fat, spell eventual shortages of food and help to bring about ecological disaster?

Think and pray

Spend a few moments thinking about this piece on cattle. Then spend a few moments praying over the thoughts you have had.

Say a prayer for all those whose livelihood has been affected by the mass culling of cattle in an attempt to eliminate BSE.

14

Waste

Each year in the UK we throw away on average five times our own weight; altogether, 25 million tons of household and commercial rubbish. Wastes are of different kinds. There are solid wastes; the contents of domestic dustbins, waste paper and old newspapers, throwaway materials, industrial and commercial wastes consisting of metals, wood and plastics, old cars, derelict houses, nuclear plants awaiting decommissioning, the detritus from coal mining and sand and gravel extraction, and just generally junk. There are liquid wastes; kitchen and bath water, human and domesticated animal sewage, the toxic remains of chemical manufacturing processes, high level, intermediate and low level nuclear wastes, among others. Thirty per cent of household waste is paper and cardboard, decaying foodstuffs 22 per cent, plastics 9 per cent, glass 9 per cent, metals 8 per cent, textiles 3 per cent and miscellaneous 18 per cent. The average household each year throws away ninety drink cans, 107 bottles and jars, seventy food cans, two trees' worth of paper and 140 kilograms of food waste.

We still dump or burn 95 per cent of our household rubbish. Some councils now distribute plastic bags for the collection of glass, paper and empty metal tins, which they collect. About half of all household waste is potentially recyclable. Even if there is no household collection, there are now usually collection points and a central dump. Much litter is thoughtlessly thrown away in parks, streets and other public places. I live near a London common; in the mornings during the summer I usually find it littered with empty bottles and other debris which people have not been bothered to dispose of properly.

In 1991 the European Union issued a directive to recycle 60 per cent of all packaging, rising to 90 per cent by the year 2000; but by 1993 only about 30 per cent was being recycled. The government has a target for 25 per cent of all wastes to be collected and recycled by councils by the year 2000. Many councils have a very, very long way still to go. By 1993 only 3 per cent of the total was being recycled. Household waste is about 300 kilograms per person a year. This works out countrywide at over 7 million tons each year. Strangely enough the amount has not increased very much over the last ten years, despite 30 per cent increase in household expenditure over this period. This is probably because there has been greater interest in recycling, packaging has become more lightweight, and plastic has often been substituted for heavier metal

Many articles are thrown away after comparatively little use because they are made in such a way that they will not last too long. Built-in obsolescence encourages greater consumption and therefore greater manufacturing profits. This applies, for example, to washing machines and other 'white goods'. It is often cheaper to buy a new article than to have an old one repaired. This is because electric and electronic products are manufactured in bulk, and cannot be repaired without specialists in their construction. This may apply to radios and television sets. It may be cheaper to provide plastic throwaway models of more expensive metal objects (such as razors and razor blades). In earlier days when objects were made to last, there was less waste of resources. Nowadays, when conspicuous consumption is thought to increase general prosperity, there is very considerable waste.

Industrial and commercial waste amounts to 85 million tons a year. Not much is recycled: 70 per cent of lead, 40 per cent of ferrous metals, 35 per cent of copper, 30 per cent of aluminium, 20 per cent of zinc. More recycling would save a great deal of energy expended in preparing these metals for manufacturing use. For example, a saucepan made from recycled aluminium requires only 5 per cent of the energy needed to make a saucepan from newly mined bauxite. Similarly 99 per cent of the energy used to make polyethylene plastic can be saved if recycled material is used; and recycled newsprint only needs a quarter of the energy required to manufacture unrecycled newsprint.

There are special problems in dealing with radioactive wastes (see under 'Nuclear power'). It is estimated that there are each year between 2 and 2.5 million tons of special wastes arising in the UK. 'Special wastes' are those which consist of or compose substances which are dangerous to life. They are subject to special conditions for their disposal. But until the 1980s, anything could be dumped in old landfill sites, and it is not easy to find out where they all are, and very expensive to take remedial action. It is still comparatively easy to dump toxic substances in unauthorized dumps, thus poisoning the ground, with the possibility of toxic metals leaching into the groundwater. Scandalous practices have been exposed in the past. Not all dumps are considered safe. Throwaway objects containing materials dangerous to life may be buried in them. Some of them emit methane gas from decomposing material, and this adds to the stock of 'greenhouse' gases. Forty-five per cent of methane gas emitted in the UK comes from landfill sites. There is a national target to reduce the total amount of waste going to landfill sites to 60 per cent of total 'arisings' by 2005. A landfill tax in the UK was introduced in 1996.

It used to be easy to dump wastes across frontiers without authorization This still happens. After 1984 the industrialized countries have agreed not to do this unless there are adequate disposal facilities, with consent on the part of the receiving country and the same controls as they apply at home. In the late 1980s nearly two million tons of waste have been recorded as exported overseas from industrialized countries.

In addition to landfill, another way of disposing of wastes is by incineration. In Switzerland, Japan and Sweden half of all municipal waste is incinerated. Often energy is recovered. Controls on air pollution from waste disposal plants have been tightened up. Among European industrial countries it is reckoned that the equivalent of 92 million barrels of oil could be produced in this way. In England there are a few waste disposal plants and plans for more; but there is not large-scale incineration.

There are many reasons why we should worry about waste. God expects us not to be wasteful. We need to conserve for posterity valuable resources. Recycling reduces energy use in manufacture, and so burns less globe-warming and non-renewable fossil fuels. Reserves of metals are limited. They are usually combined with other substances in crystalline, inorganic compounds. Refining these metals already uses up enormous amounts of energy. Resources should be distinguished from reserves. The former is used to designate the total amount of metal ores in the earth's crust. Most of these are in such dilute concentrations that it is not economic to extract them. Conventional ores of precious metals (what we call reserves) are likely to be used up by the middle of the next century. Then silicate metals will have to be broken down to extract further supplies of these metals. This will require between 100 and 1,000 times more energy than present processes. It will probably never be worthwhile. Substitute materials will have to be used. Recycled materials are much cheaper in energy consumption than unrecycled. And throwaway materials, as we have also seen, can produce dangerous pollution. These are three good reasons why we should not waste materials, and why we should wherever possible recycle goods. A fourth is that mining new supplies often disturbs animal habitats. For example, bauxite (for aluminium) is often extracted from tropical forest land. Finally, it is cheaper to recycle now than to leave a future generation to clean up the mess we have made.

Luke 15:11–20

And [Jesus] said, 'There was a man who had two sons; and the younger of them said to his father, "Father, give me the share of property that falls to me." And he divided his living between them. Not many days later, the younger son gathered all he had and took his journey into a far country, and there he squandered his property in loose living. And when he had spent everything, a great famine arose in that country, and he began to be in want. So he went and joined himself to one of the citizens of that country, who sent him into his fields to feed swine. And he would gladly have fed on the pods that the swine ate; and no one gave him anything. But when he came to himself he said, "How many of my father's hired servants have bread enough and to spare, but I perish with hunger! I will arise and go to my father, and I will say to him, 'Father, I have sinned against heaven and before you; I am no longer worthy to be called your son; treat me as one of your hired servants.' " And he arose and came to his father...'

Comment on the reading

This is probably the best-known of all Jesus' parables, the story of the prodigal son. The parable was told to show the loving forgiveness of God to all who repent and turn to him. Interest is naturally focused on the return home of the younger son. But the reading has been chosen here for a different purpose: to show the reason why he was forced to do this. The younger son had asked for his share of his inheritance before his father had died; and when he had it, he wasted it. He had been thoughtless of the implications of what he had been doing. He had not taken seriously the fact that it was an inheritance, which he was expected to hand on to the next generation as his father had handed it on to him. He had preferred the pleasures it would bring him momentarily, and he had been forgetful of the future.

The chief purpose of the parable is to show us what God is like. But we can draw something else out of it as well, and use it as a parable of the way in which we tend to treat our present-day inheritance of the earth and the rivers and the oceans, and all the wildlife that lives there. We too are thoughtless of the implications of what we are doing. We do not take seriously the fact that it is an inheritance entrusted to us, which we are expected to hand on to the next generations as it has been handed on to us. We too prefer the benefits which it brings to us here and now, and we are forgetful of what will happen as a result in the future.

The younger son wasted his inheritance. We live in a throwaway society, in which waste is a prime characteristic.

Things to do and not to do

As individuals we can greatly help to eliminate waste. Here are the five Rs which give the rules of conservation:

1. Refuse to be given unnecessary packaging.
2. Return bottles whenever possible—and if possible buy returnable bottles.
3. Reuse items wherever possible (e.g., envelopes, bottles and plastic bags).
4. Repair things rather than throw them away.
5. Recycle metal cans, paper and bottles.

A prayer

O God, you have given us so much in the resources of your world. Help us to value them and not to waste them, and to enable them to be used by those who come after us.

15

Gardens

Gardens, however small, are very popular in the UK, even though only two out of three houses have them. When the UK's gardens are aggregated, they cover 1.5 million acres, so it is important that they should be well-treated. People are often prepared to spend large sums of money on their gardens, as sales in garden centres prove. In urban houses, flowers bring natural beauty into the living room. Gardens can produce fresh fruit and vegetables, perhaps organically grown. Many plants have beautiful scents. Gardens attract birds and bees and wildlife. Flowers, plants and trees have a natural beauty. Their variety of shapes and colours delight us. We like to watch the natural processes of germination and growth. People who have to work indoors find pleasure in spending leisure hours in the open air, tending their gardens. It is refreshing to renew contact with nature. Surely this is healthy living, conducive to conservation and assisting the natural ecosystems of life?

Unfortunately some gardening activities are not in the best interests of the environment as a whole. For example, a large number of bags of peat are sold in garden centres. This is helping to endanger a valuable but diminishing national and international resource.

The use of alternatives to peat actually has government approval. Most British peatbogs are situated in the north, particularly in the north of Scotland, where they are not suitable for commercial use. But the 'Lowland Raised Bogs' of England are threatened with extinction. Only 5,000 hectares of this primary bog is left; and once removed, it cannot be regenerated.

Peat is not a soil nutrient, but it has a great capacity for retaining and releasing water and also for retaining air, rather like a sponge. It is also very long lasting if it is not dried out (and that is why it is popular for the garden). Peatbogs are important. They comprise unique habitats for certain kinds of wildlife, and for some species the peatbog is their last refuge. They are a valuable genetic source for the future. They act as natural reservoirs of highly purified water. Our wetlands have a vital ecological function. They also store and release carbon dioxide, although the mechanisms by which they do this are not yet fully understood. Alternatives to peat in gardens include mushroom compost, bark and coir (coconut fibre). These are usually available in garden centres: if not, they can be requested.

Pesticides are commonly used in gardens. Insects and wildlife which destroy plants and vegetables are rightly called pests. Viruses can also infect plants and trees. Without pesticides a third of crops and food in store would be lost; and without pesticides many garden plants and vegetables would wither and die. Quite apart from the vast amounts which farmers and professional nurserymen spend on pesticides, sales for private gardens amount to £30m a year. They are certainly needed. Some of them, especially those derived from natural sources like pyrethrum, do no lasting harm. Others are very toxic. They linger in the soil. They can affect wildlife, and even human beings. It is the synthetic pesticides and fertilizers of which we should beware.

Just as organic farmers use only organic substances in their farming, the amateur gardener can do the same. Compost enriches the soil: it can be made by putting vegetable peelings, grass cuttings and other organic material in a compost heap or a compost tumbler. There are other ways in which we can help nature. Some plant species attract wildlife, and these species can be planted. Toxic substances such as paint or oil can be carefully disposed of, and not left in the ground to poison the soil. Those who complain of the way in which big business treats the environment must be careful to see that their own lifestyle does not encourage waste or environmental degradation. Often gardens have bits of brick and building materials embedded in the soil, left over from house building. Topsoil needs to be carefully treated and extraneous bodies removed. It is very precious, and it contains an amalgam of micro-organisms and trace elements and inorganic substances. Topsoil takes many years to form, and so it must be carefully preserved. Most gardeners know that. Of course much good land has already been wasted; but what about the 1.5 million acres of gardens in the UK? We need to take care that we do not unwittingly damage the soil.

Even though we may buy land and own its title deeds, it only belongs to us legally. It really belongs to God. In that sense we are its trustees. The point is made clearly in the Old Testament. Under the law of jubilee the land would remain fallow in the seventh year. 'In the seventh year there shall be a sabbath of solemn rest for the land, a sabbath to the Lord; you shall not sow your field or prune your vineyard' (Leviticus 25:4). After fifty years all land had to be returned to its original owner. 'You shall hallow the fiftieth year, and proclaim liberty throughout the land to all its inhabitants: it shall be a jubilee to you, when each of you shall return to his property and each of you shall return to his family' (Leviticus 25:10). This makes it clear that we have a duty to conserve the soil and to pass it on in good shape to future generations.

The way in which people treat their gardens often gives a good indication of their true attitudes towards conservation.

Song of Solomon 4:11—5:1

Your lips distil nectar, my bride; honey and milk are under your tongue; the scent of your garments is like the scent of Lebanon. A garden locked is my sister, my bride, a garden locked, a fountain sealed. Your shoots are an orchard of pomegranates with all choicest fruits, henna with nard, nard and saffron, calamus and cinnamon, with all trees of frankincense, myrrh and aloes, with all chief spices—a garden fountain, a well of living water, and flowing streams from Lebanon.

Awake, O north wind, and come, O south wind! Blow upon my garden, let its fragrance be wafted abroad. Let my beloved come to his garden, and eat its choicest fruits.

I come to my garden, my sister, my bride, I gather my myrrh with my spice, I eat my honeycomb with my honey, I drink my wine with my milk.

Eat, O friends, and drink; drink deeply, O lovers!

Comment on the reading

The Song of Solomon has often been attributed to Solomon himself but the presence of a Persian word (the word for 'orchard' in the reading) together with a Greek word also transliterated into Hebrew suggests rather a date around AD300. The Song has been variously interpreted. Some have thought it is a dialogue between Solomon, a maiden and her beloved, with Solomon trying to woo her into his harem. Others have understood it as an allegory, either of a loving God and his chosen people Israel, or of Christ and his bride the Church. It is, however, best to take it at face value as a love poem or a collection of love songs. In the reading the bride is described by the imagery of a garden. It brings together the beauties of nature and the mystery of human love. After aromatic and sweet-smelling herbs, the description reaches a climax in cool running water, aiming to do justice to the charms of the bride. The poetry is erotic, and gives the lie to those who hold that the scriptures are unfriendly towards sexual love between husband and wife.

This reading has been chosen simply to indicate our love of a cultivated garden. The author of the Song of Solomon could think of nothing more appropriate by which to describe a beloved maiden. In the ancient world gardens were much loved. The Bible begins in a garden, the garden of Eden: 'the Lord God took the man and put him in the garden of Eden to till it and to keep it' (Genesis 2:15). The hanging gardens of Babylon were one of the seven wonders of the ancient world. Isaiah describes the daughter of Zion as 'like a booth in a vineyard, like a lodge in a garden of cucumbers' (Isaiah 1:8). All gardens need watering, especially in the Middle East, and a watered garden was a symbol of the blessing of God. 'The Lord will guide you continually,' said the prophet Isaiah, 'and satisfy your desire with good things, and make your bones strong; and you shall be like a watered garden' (Isaiah 58:11); words echoed by Jeremiah when prophesying the redemption of Israel: 'They shall come and sing aloud on the height of Zion, and they shall be radiant over the goodness of the Lord... their life shall be like a watered garden' (Jeremiah 31:12).

Jesus was buried in a garden. 'In the place where he was crucified there was a garden, and in the garden a new tomb where no one had even been laid' (John 19:41). It was there that we are told Mary Magdalene was the first to see the risen Lord, not realizing who he was but 'supposing him to the gardener' (John 20:15).

But gardens too, for all their beauty and refreshment, can be places of wickedness. Isaiah condemns the Jews when he speaks of 'a people who provoke me to my face continually, sacrificing in gardens and burning incense upon bricks' (Isaiah 65:3). He was speaking of pagan worship; but we today, for all our love of gardens, could be provoking God because in our gardens, albeit unwittingly, we may be harming our environment.

A prayer of thanks for creation

O God, we thank you for this earth, our home; for the wide sky and the blessed sun, for the salt sea and the running water, for the everlasting hills and the never resting winds, for trees and the common grass underfoot. We thank you for our senses by which we hear the song of the birds, and see the splendour of the summer fields, and taste of the autumn fruits, and rejoice in the feel of the snow, and smell the breath of spring. Grant us a heart wide open to all this beauty; and save our souls from being so blind that we pass unseeing when even the common thornbush is aflame with your glory, O God our creator, who lives and reigns for ever and ever.

Walter Rauschenbusch

16

Geophysiology

Physiology is the science of functions and phenomena of living organisms, and the prefix 'geo' indicates that here it refers to the whole planet. I have used this awkward word 'geophysiology' to describe the subject of this section, because people are nervous of the word 'Gaia', the word chosen by Dr James Lovelock, FRS, to describe his 'Gaia hypothesis'. People fight shy of the word Gaia because they are frightened that it has something to do with the 'New Age' movement and the goddess called Gaia. It is, in fact, quite biblical to speak of 'Mother Earth', because the scriptures describe how the earth 'brought forth' life (Genesis 1:24) and the Hebrew word used is that of birth. It is quite appropriate. Life started in the oceans, just as life starts in the waters of the womb, which have to be regulated at the right temperature for life to develop; and life is sustained by a mother's oxygen. But the scriptures are clear that when Mother Earth brought forth life, it all happened at the command of God the Creator, who initiated the whole process.

James Lovelock's 'Gaia' has nothing to do with the 'New Age' movement. It is a purely scientific hypothesis. This is that the earth is alive, in the sense that it regulates itself in such a way that it remains comfortable for life. It is notoriously difficult to define life. If by life is meant the capacity to reproduce, then Gaia is certainly not alive. If by life is meant the capacity to develop according to one's genes, again Gaia is not alive. In what sense then can Gaia said to be alive? It has evolved self-regulating mechanisms which enable it to remain stable over millions of years, and living organisms as well as inorganic matter assist this process. An organism can be said to be alive if it has outer limits and boundaries, if it takes in energy (either as sunlight or energy stored in food), excretes waste products, does not run itself down, but remains stable, whatever be the change in external conditions. This is what happens with the biosphere. William Hutton (1726–97), the father of geology, called the earth a 'superorganism'.

Because Gaia is such a misleading term, with the name of a Greek goddess giving the impression of earth worship, an alternative word has been used to describe the study of this process: geophysiology. Physiology is the study of the systems that comprise a living organism. It is a holistic discipline. What physiology is to a living organism, geophysiology is for the superorganism which is the biosphere.

There is no need to enter here into scientific technicalities. It is enough to point out that no arguments have been found which invalidate Dr Lovelock's hypothesis. And the earth has remained in a stable state. We have had a constant atmosphere for 3.5 billion years, despite a 25 per cent rise in the sun's luminosity. (A little more oxygen would produce unstoppable forest fires: a little less, and one could not make fire by striking a match.) The climate has remained for hundreds of millions of years comfortable for life. The oceans have remained salty within very narrow limits, necessary for the continuance of marine life, despite huge quantities of salt flowing into the sea from rivers, and up from below from fissures in the earth's crust.

So the earth—or rather the biosphere, to be precise—is rather like the body which Paul described in his first letter to the Corinthians. The elements cooperate, as it were, to make conditions comfortable for life. Systems appear which keep things stable. Dr Lovelock has used a simple model to explain the kind of way these systems work. He calls it the 'daisyland parable'. He imagines a planet filled with only two plants, black daisies and white daisies. Black daisies absorb the heat, white daisies reflect it back into space. If the climate gets too hot, this will kill off the black daisies, because they will absorb too much heat. So the white daisies will begin to dominate the vegetation. This will cool down the climate, as the white daisies increase in number. But if they increase too much, too much heat will be reflected back into space, and the white daisies will die of cold, and black daisies will take their place. And so this make-believe planet would be kept in equilibrium by this self-generated climate mechanism. In our real world, there are many such mechanisms at work. Similar processes enable trace elements to be transferred from ocean to land.

Although these processes are described in a strictly scientific manner, Christians may rightly regard them as part of the providential ordering of God in his creation of the universe.

Paul wrote that the less honourable parts of the body are given greater honour, and that the parts which seem weaker are indispensable. That is very true of the earth's body. A lot of these systems involve some of the smallest organisms that exist. From the weathering of an exposed rock of a continental mountain to the deposition of algal shells as limestone on the ocean floor, there is an unceasing intervention by the smallest of creatures (diatoms and coccolithopores).

Bacteria perform other important functions. For example, the photosynthesizers on the surface of land or sea release oxygen into the air and remove carbon dioxide. A world with just photosynthesizing bacteria would be unstable: they would lock up in their bodies too much carbon, and the planet would freeze. Bacteria called methanogens ensure that this does not happen. These are the fermenters which digest organic matter and turn it into carbon dioxide. Bacterial groups, the lowliest parts of planet earth's body, have sustained the stability of the planet for over three and a half billion years.

Ecology shows that the stability of the planet is maintained by the interaction of all its different parts. Most of this is inorganic (dead) matter, but plants and living organisms play their part. Life can only exist on the surface of the earth, with the atmosphere above and the earth's crust beneath. It is rather like the huge redwoods in the USA, where the bark is dead and so is the wood of the tree; but a thin layer under the bark is alive, and feeds on the dead matter within and outside.

The earth has a natural stability and human beings are tending to disrupt it. Global warming is one of the results. The earth is beginning to suffer from a kind of fever. Like all illnesses, the cause is very different from the symptoms. If a human body has on its skin more than a certain amount of first degree burns it cannot survive. The stripping of the forests and the turning of so much land into pasture or croplands may be compared to first degree burns. A planetary fever ensues. A person with a fever requires a well-ventilated bedroom; but the earth suffers from global warming gases. Or, to take another illustration, some people suffer from heartburn as a result of acid indigestion. Acid rain is causing a similar kind of illness on planet earth.

God gave to mankind dominion over the earth. This is an obvious fact of life. But dominion does not give the right to behave like a dictator, with human beings disregarding the general welfare in favour of their own aggrandizement. This is what is happening today on the planet. It is causing instability to the ecosystems of the world. It is disrupting the equilibrium which has been so carefully nurtured by the self-assembling mechanisms which have been regulating the planet and giving it stability for hundreds of millions of years. If it is true that the biosphere is alive in the sense defined above, it may be able to adapt its mechanisms to take account of mankind's depredations. But the human species is not immortal. Just as the human body strives to get rid of an infection which threatens its life, so the planet may rid itself of mankind. This would happen from natural processes, such as the increasing reduction in human sperm count. If it were to happen, mankind would be bringing upon itself the judgment of God.

1 Corinthians 12:14–26

> The body does not consist of one member but of many. If the foot should say, 'Because I am not a hand, I do not belong to the body,' that would not make it any less a part of the body. And if the ear should say, 'Because I am not an eye, I do not belong to the body,' that would not make it any less a part of the body. If the whole body were an eye, where would be the hearing? If the whole body were an ear, where would be the sense of smell? But as it is, God arranged the organs in the body, each one of them, as he chose. If all were a single organ, where would the body be? As it is, there are many parts, yet one body. The eye cannot say to the hand, 'I have no need of you,' nor again the head to the feet, 'I have no need of you.' On the contrary, the parts of the body which seem to be weaker are indispensable, and those parts of the body which we think less honourable we invest with greater honour, and our unpresentable parts are treated with greater modesty, which our more presentable parts do not require. But God has so composed the body, giving the greater honour to the inferior part, that there may be no discord in the body, but that the members may have the same care for one another. If one member suffers, all suffer together; if one member is honoured, all rejoice together.

Comment on the reading

St Paul, writing to the church in Corinth which he founded, introduces this picture of the body in illustration of his image of the Church as the body of Christ, with each member interdependent on others, and all working in harmony together. He was explaining that the whole Church is a divinely created social organism.

Just how literally he intended his image of the body to be taken it is hard to say. In the letter to the Ephesians, we read 'he has put all things under his feet and has made him the head over all things for the church, which is his body, the fullness of him who fills all in all' (Ephesians 1:22). Here Christ is not the body as a whole but the head of the body which is the Church. The Church is the whole body of Christians, rather than just the local church. But when St Paul wrote to the Corinthians, he did not distinguish Christ as head of the body, and it was the local church that he meant when he wrote: 'Now you are the body of Christ and individually members of it' (1 Corinthians 12:27). These apparent loose ends need not bother us, providing we do not take the analogy of the body too literally. It is perhaps best to understand the phrase 'body of Christ' as meaning that the Church is the instrument through which Christ works, and the means by which he is known and recognized.

There were, we know, factions in Corinth. St Paul was trying to show the Christians there that they must all work together, and live in harmony. In the days of St Paul Christians and Jews believed that God had directly fashioned the human body in this way. Today we live in an era when the idea of evolution is generally accepted (although not necessarily the neo-Darwinian view of evolution). So we interpret the words 'God arranged the organs in the body' to mean not that he directly fashioned them in this way, but that he is the architect and Creator of the universe in which living things (including human beings) have evolved in this way under his providence.

In writing of giving honour to the less honourable parts of the body, Paul was probably referring to the less gifted members of the Church. Nobody may look down on a fellow Christian because of his or her lower social status or lower intelligence or other gifts. There must rather be positive discrimination, so that the least honoured is given the most honour.

This passage has not been chosen because of its reference to the Church, although it contains important lessons for the Church to learn. It has been chosen because St Paul's whole analogy of a living body is particularly applicable to the biosphere in which we live. As we might expect, that which is relevant to the sphere of divine revelation in the Church is also directly relevant to the natural world in which we live. 'Biosphere' is a word which includes not only biota (or living things) but also the environment in which they live. St Paul's imagery of the different organs of the body and the giving of honour to those that are least honoured is just as applicable to the biosphere as a whole as it is to the Church. Paul wrote: 'If the whole body were an eye, where would be the hearing?' Sometimes we behave as though we thought the whole body consisted only of human beings, with the result that we find ourselves in trouble through ignoring the rest of the biosphere on which we depend for our continued existence.

For reflection

The world is charged with the glory of God.
It will flame out, like shining from shook foil;
It gathers to a greatness, like the ooze of oil
Crushed. Why do men then now not reck his rod?
Generations have trod, have trod, have trod;
And all is seared with trade; bleared, smeared with toil;
And wears man's smudge and shares man's smell: the soil
Is bare now, nor can foot feel, being shod.

And for all this, nature is never spent;
There lives the dearest freshness deep down things.
And though the last lights off the black West went

Oh, morning, at the brown brink eastward, springs—
Because the Holy Ghost over the bent
World broods with warm breast and with ah! bright wings.

Gerard Manley Hopkins, 'God's Grandeur'

17

Matter and materialism

Until recently the parable of the rich fool has been particularly appropriate to the European agricultural situation, with its wine lakes and beef mountains which have had to be stored in aircraft hangars—although the world situation has recently emptied the large stocks of 'intervention' foodstuffs. Storing up possessions is often a sign of greed and covetousness. A warning against covetousness is specially timely today, when rich nations wish to get even richer. The status of individuals is often judged by the value of their possessions. The basis of most advertising is to increase consumption and to foster a desire to have a higher standard of living. Political parties vie with one another to produce a programme which will be thought to increase prosperity. We have become an acquisitive society. Increasingly materialism strengthens its hold, often at the expense of quality of life. Britain is for ever taking its economic temperature. GNP (Gross National Product) and RPI (Retail Price Index) seem to have become national preoccupations. Countries which excel in these often lag far down in the HDI (Human Development Index). This measures such matters as health and education, but its findings are seldom publicized.

Needless and conspicuous consumption is often the result of greed and covetousness. It also causes a waste of resources. It requires greater landfill for the disposal of obsolete goods and throwaway objects. Much energy is employed in the manufacture of these objects of consumption, usually from non-renewable sources. The transport of these goods from factory to retail outlets, usually by lorries on overcrowded roads, adds to the expenditure of non-renewable fossil fuels. People only walk a quarter of the distance they did in the past: they prefer the comfort of mechanical means of transport which use non-renewable energy. Jesus makes it clear that materialism means spiritual impoverishment. At the same time it usually involves environmental damage. This is not to say that concern for the environment is opposed to development. It is not. It actually creates employment through the measures which need to be taken to avoid or clean up environmental damage. But it does mean that development must be sustainable.

Materialism is the belief that material possessions are the most important in life. On this view a man's life does consist in the abundance of things he possesses. Such a view often stems from a philosophical materialism, the belief that spiritual values have no basis in reality. Matter, it is thought, is the only thing which really exists. Even human beings are in essence no more than the sum of their material parts. Spirituality is ultimately reducible to physics. This is, of course, directly opposed to the Christian belief that the Spirit of God fills the universe and upholds it. Human beings are not just physical objects. They are indwelt by the Holy Spirit of God. They are people who are made in the image of God.

Because the Christian faith utterly rejects materialism in both senses of the word described above, this does not involve a contempt for matter. On the contrary, God himself created matter. He saw everything that he had made, and behold it was very good (Genesis 1:31). Christianity is the religion of the incarnation. At the heart of the faith is the conviction that God took flesh in Jesus Christ. Flesh is matter; and if God honoured matter in such a way, so also do Christians. It is part of the Christian faith that God communicates with human beings through sacraments. These, in the words of the Prayer Book catechism, are 'outward and visible signs of an inward and spiritual grace given unto us, ordained by Christ himself, as a means whereby we receive the same, and a pledge to assure us thereof'. As we human beings express ourselves by outward signs, so too God communicates himself to us in this way.

It has been rightly said that Christianity is one of the most materialist of all religions. Issues of the environment concern matter in its various forms; gases, water, metals, topsoil, micro-organisms and so on. It is sometimes said that a spiritual religion should not concern itself overmuch with such material things. But God created matter, and honoured it by assuming it in the person of his Son. It follows that Christians should be involved with material concerns as well as with spiritual issues. They should be concerned primarily with the attitudes expressed by the ways in which people treat matter, whether this is organic or inorganic matter. But they should also be concerned about the practical consequences of the way in which matter is treated, including environmental damage.

The natural sciences investigate matter in its various forms. They examine matter at various levels of existence: physically, chemically, biologically and so on. Geophysiology combines many scientific disciplines, being concerned with the various systems which maintain the life of the planet. All things that come from God must be good. So there can be no scientific knowledge that it is not good for us in principle to know. This knowledge may be abused; but that is another issue. The knowledge itself, because it is knowledge of God's world, must be good.

The Christian faith does not hold that everything in the world is predetermined. It therefore requires empirical investigation of the world, not merely logical thought, to unravel the regularities of nature which God has brought into being. It follows that scientific investigation of matter in all its forms is consonant with the Christian faith. It is no coincidence that the serious study of the natural sciences arose within Christian culture.

Technology is the harnessing of scientific knowledge to practical ends. A very early example of technology is the invention of the wheel, which has brought enormous saving of labour: without wheels everything would have had to be carried or pushed.

Nowadays in the Western world there is very sophisticated technology. The washing machine and the vacuum cleaner, the refrigerator and the freezer have brought great blessing to mankind. Medical technology has cured illness, removed sources of pain and enabled people to live longer. Mass production of food has enabled millions more people to be fed. There is vastly increased mobility and much speedier communication. Technology must not be undervalued because it is concerned with material objects.

On the other hand technology can be abused. Power and energy can be harnessed for evil ends (such as nuclear weapons or chemical warfare). It is also an abuse to introduce inappropriate technology. Some inventions merely waste non-renewable energy in performing tasks which could easily be undertaken manually (for example, electric carving knives). Smaller-scale technology is often needed in developing countries. E.F. Schumacher coined the phrase 'Small is beautiful', meaning that large-scale technology is often unsuitable for small scale use. For example, to produce electricity by photoelectric cells from sunlight is more appropriate to peasant farmers in primitive tropical surroundings than centralized supplies of energy from a large power station; and this does not use non-renewable forms of energy. But the misuse of technology must not obscure its great usefulness. For example, new technology in the building of houses can greatly reduce the need for indoor artificial heating.

Materialism is bad; but matter is good, and knowledge of matter is good, and matter can be harnessed by technology for good ends. This is badly needed to ensure that the planet can live healthily, and support the large numbers of human beings alive on it without the destruction of its vital systems.

Luke 12:13–26

One of the multitude said to him, 'Teacher, bid my brother divide the inheritance with me.' But he said to him, 'Man, who made me a judge or a divider over you?' And he said to them, 'Take heed, and beware of all covetousness; for a man's life does not consist in the abundance of his possessions.' And he told them a parable, saying, 'The land of a rich man brought forth plentifully; and he thought to himself, "What shall I do, for I have nowhere to store my crops?" And he said, "I will do this: I will pull down my barns, and build larger ones; and there I will store all my grain and my goods. And I will say to my soul, Soul, you have ample goods laid up for many years; take your ease, eat, drink, be merry." But God said to him, "Fool! This night your soul is required of you; and the things you have prepared, whose will they be?" So is he who lays up treasure for himself, and is not rich toward God.'

And he said to his disciples, 'Therefore I tell you, do not be anxious about your life, what you shall eat, nor about your body, what you shall put on. For life is more than food, and the body more than clothing. Consider the ravens: they neither sow nor reap, they have neither storehouse nor barn, and yet God feeds them. Of how much more value are you than the birds! And which of you by being anxious can add a cubit to his span of life? If then you are not able to do as small a thing as that, why are you anxious about the rest?'

Comment on the reading

Jesus on one occasion declined to rule on a matter of law, because the law can only put restrictions on people: it cannot alter the attitudes of the heart which are the main determinant of human conduct. Jesus discerned that in the case brought before him it was covetousness which led to the request to him to divide the inheritance. So he refused to act as a judge in the legal matter of inheritance of money and property. For those who enter the kingdom and live by its values, legislation ceases to be relevant as when Jesus said that Moses only permitted divorce 'for the hardness of your hearts': according to the values of the kingdom, marriage was to be permanent (Mark 10:5–8). Covetousness is a bad disposition of the heart. It is denounced again and again in the scriptures, both in the Old Testament. (e.g. 'From the least to the greatest of them, every one is greedy for unjust gain', Jeremiah 6:13) and in the New Testament ('They were filled with all manner of wickedness, evil, covetousness, malice', Romans 1:29). Jesus in our reading gave a graphic illustration of the rich fool who discovered all too late that he had spent his life amassing things which he could not take with him when he died. His consuming interest was in amassing things which were external to himself. His death exposed his own terrible poverty, despite his material wealth. He had hoped that this wealth would bring him security, so that he could live a happy care-free existence. But not for long! He was to die that night, and that exposed the hollowness of his intentions.

Concern over material things is not merely for the rich. It can also apply to the poor. So Jesus warns against anxiety over material things. The passage has sometimes been understood as a command to take no thought for the future. But that is not the meaning of the Greek word translated here 'be anxious'. It would be ludicrous not to take steps now to ensure sufficient water for the future in a time of drought, or sufficient food in a time of food shortage. Equally it would be foolish not to take thought for the future of the planet as a result of present actions. What Jesus was doing was to warn against worrying about the future. Worry never helps. It fixes our attention on the cause of our worry so that we tend to forget God. However important environmental matters—and the whole aim of this book is to show their very great importance—they are not as important as God.

A prayer

Lord God of earth and heaven, you know better than we that plenty can be as great a spiritual burden as poverty. Forgive us... who have so many blessings, for taking them so much for granted... For thinking that they are ours to do with as we please... For squandering so many of them in such irresponsible and irretrievable ways.

Remind us that your Word is more precious by far than the things we treasure... more powerful by far than the people and policies that we trust... more promising by far than the schemes we try for gaining the world while giving up our souls.

William Russell

18

The economics of the environment

The price of something is decided by the amount which people are prepared to pay in order to purchase it. It is normally assumed that the mechanism of the market should determine the cost of what is bought and sold. If there is a glut of something, its price will nosedive. If goods are in short supply, their price will rise. If there are monopolies, there may have to be regulation to ensure that a fair price is charged. For the sake of the poor, it may be necessary to regulate and possibly to subsidize goods which are necessary for survival. It may even be necessary sometimes to provide subsidies for such necessities as travel to and from work, so that those whose situation forces them to live at a distance from their work place are not unduly penalized. But by and large it is commonly assumed that the market decides the price of what is bought and sold.

But the market only shows what goods or services are worth to people here and now. The future is not taken into account, except in so far as the price may be expected to rise or fall in the future. There are also hidden future costs of which people may not even be aware, but which some future person will have to pay if they are not paid by the buyer at the time of purchase. Many things cause pollution, and sooner or later there will be costs to be paid in eradicating that pollution. Would it not be more just if these costs were paid at the time of purchase, rather than suffering the pollution that is caused, and then leaving someone else to pay for cleaning it up later? Does not the market give a false price in this perspective? Is it not rather like false weights or false measures on the scales? Is not the present situation unjust; and if it is unjust, is it not an abomination to the Lord?

This applies even to humble objects. For example, every time milk is bought, a container is bought too, either a bottle or a container. These have to be taken away later to a landfill site or reused or recycled. (A milk bottle is used on average fourteen times until it gets broken or thrown away.) When tinned goods are bought, someone eventually has to pay for their removal and hopefully for their recycling. Council tax pays for some of this, but not all.

The same point applies to grander products. When electricity is used in the home, it has often been produced in coal-burning electricity generators belching out chemical pollution which causes acid rain. Scrubbers could be fitted to eliminate these noxious gases at source. This might add to the cost of electricity, but would that not be more just than leaving the countryside blighted and making others in the future pay the costs? Whenever gas or petrol or coal is burnt, globe-warming carbon dioxide is released into the atmosphere. Someone later is going to suffer the cost of altered climate and weather; and this cost will be worldwide and not confined within national boundaries. Tax on petrol has been increased in the UK partly for this reason. But coal, which releases more sulphurous gases than oil or gas, has no such tax added to it.

Fossil fuels are irreplaceable. They take millions of years to produce. Some of them will become in shorter supply sometime in the next century: in any case, they cannot last for ever. If it is left to market forces to decide their price, this could result in profligate use by people able to afford now to buy as much as they want, as happens in the USA today, while people in the future will have to pay very high prices for a diminishing resource. We cannot assume that by that time some other comparable cheap fuel will have been produced: there is no sign of that today. It could be said that to charge market prices for fossil fuels is unjust to future generations. It is not so very different from using false weights and false balances.

Is it unjust to deprive future generations of goods unless it is certain that there will be an adequate replacement? The needs of the future are not more important than the needs of the present. To deprive present people of things which are essential is to ensure that there will not be any future people to use them! Conservation should not be at the expense of human beings presently alive. If irreplaceable commodities can never be used in the present because future generations will be deprived of them, that means that no one can ever use them, because there will always be a future generation! But they must not be wasted, or used in a prodigal manner.

What is needed is sustainable development. Undeveloped nations naturally wish to develop. Developed countries naturally wish to develop further. To deny this is to go against the grain of human nature. What is required is development which is sustainable and which does not diminish total capital resources, whether natural, human, or man-made. Only so is it possible to leave the world for the next generation in as good shape as we found it, and give them the same opportunities as are presently enjoyed.

Indonesia is a good example of development that is unsustainable in the developing world. It wants improved medical and educational services and a higher standard of living, and it is cutting down its rainforests to provide capital for this development. But when the forests are gone, the capital has gone. Economic calculations have been made that if trees were cut down in a way that was sustainable, the capital tied up in the products of the remaining forest, together with the value of the species found in them and the forest's function in preserving climate and weather and topsoil would be greater than the capital value of the wholesale destruction of their forests.

The same argument could be applied closer to home. How can it be decided where houses are to be built, and how much should be charged for the land? It might be said that if a house is built on a site with a good view, people might be prepared to pay £1,000 for the view, and so that should be added to the price. But this would only affect the buyer and the seller. If the house were built, the view would be lost to the public so long as the house stood, and the value of that loss cannot be accurately estimated in terms of money at all. There are those who say that parts of the beautiful British countryside have already been permanently ruined by this kind of attempted cost benefit analysis.

There is a distinction between value and valuation. Value is what something is intrinsically worth: valuation is the cash value which people would now pay. The one cannot always be translated into the other. The desirability of new motorways has been calculated on the basis of the cash value of time saved and accidents prevented. This was used on the Okehampton motorway in Devon. But it is not possible to put a value on noise, or on the intrinsic beauty of countryside like that of Dartmoor in which there is ugly visual intrusion. As the Indian Chief Seattle said to the President of the United States of America, 'How can you buy or sell the sky, the warmth of the land? The idea is strange to us. If we do not own the freshness of the air and the sparkle of the water, how can you buy them?'

The Christian faith holds that intrinsic values are more important than financial valuation. Because Christianity is a religion of incarnation, material things are very important to it. But decision-making about the environment should not be determined only by money. Decision-making involves judgment, and that judgment must include values as well as valuation.

Deuteronomy 25:13–16

'You shall not have in your bag two kinds of weights, a large and a small. You shall not have in your house two kinds of measures, a large and a small. A full and just weight you shall have, a full and just measure you shall have; that your days may be prolonged in the land which the Lord your God gives you. For all who do such things, all who act dishonestly, are an abomination to the Lord your God.'

Comment on the reading

In a primitive community such as that in which the book of Deuteronomy was written, many purchases must have been made by barter as well as by money. Commercial honesty demands just weights, not lighter weights for selling and heavier weights for purchase. The scales must have been of paramount importance for the same reason, to ensure that the purchaser and the vendor got proper value.

Insistence on just weights and a fair balance is found frequently in the Old Testament. The warning is found in the Wisdom literature: 'Diverse weights are an abomination to the Lord, and false scales are not good' (Proverbs 20:23). According to Moses, 'You shall do no wrong in judgment, in measures of length or weight or quantity. You shall have just balances, just weights, a just ephah, and a just hin: I am the Lord your God, who brought you out of the land of Egypt' (Leviticus 19:35–36). Gratitude for what God has done should prompt obedience to God's demand for strict justice. A rather different reason is given in our reading from Deuteronomy, a prudential looking forward to the future rather than gratitude for the past. Its implication is that because God is just, he will reward the just with long life. 'A full and just weight you shall have, a full and just measure you shall have; that your days may be prolonged in the land which the Lord your God gives you' (Deuteronomy 25:15).

A false weight and short measures were a form of cheating.

They were tantamount to theft, against which the scriptures often warned. Again and again, in the Old Testament and the New Testament, there is a warning against theft. It forms part of the Ten Commandments. 'You shall not steal' (Exodus 20:15) is repeated in the teaching of Jesus (Matthew 19:18) and found in the teaching of St Paul (Romans 13:9). Theft is taking what does not belong to one. False weights and measures mean taking money or goods from others that rightly do not belong to one. The argument needs to be taken a step further. It is unjust to force others to pay expenses which one incurs oneself.

A prayer

Forgive us, Lord, for the damage we have done to the earth.
Forgive us that the rivers and seas have been polluted by the waste of our civilization.
Forgive us that the air has been turned foul by burning fuel and radioactive emissions.
Forgive us that flowers, fauna and wild creatures have become extinct through our relentless invasion of their natural habitat.
Forgive us that we have often valued profit more than the quality of the environment in which people have to live.

From *Further Everyday Prayers*, Mowbray

Help us, Lord, to live in a way that is fair to posterity.

19

International cooperation

How can the planet regain its health, and how can environmental damage be ended? Individuals cannot achieve this on their own, although it will require the cooperation of individuals. Countries cannot achieve this on their own because environmental damage often knows no frontiers, although the commitment of each country will be required. Most of the planet consists not of land but of ocean; and the ocean does not belong to any one nation outside its territorial limits. Clearly international cooperation is vital, not only with regard to the oceans, but also for the coordination of policies between countries. Otherwise countries which do not have policies which are environmentally friendly would gain an unfair advantage over those countries which do put into practice such policies. Competition would probably force them to change back to their bad old ways.

Paul asserted that all human beings are kinsmen (Acts 17:26). We can all trace a common descent back to the origin of mankind. All mankind are brothers and sisters, for all are the children of God. But is it possible in practice to achieve environmental cooperation between nations? Are the flaws in human nature so great that all attempts to achieve environmental cooperation are bound to fail? The League of Nations was formed to prevent war; but it failed and had to be disbanded. The United Nations was formed for the same purpose. It has not failed, but it would be hard to affirm that it flourishes. Will not the same fate overtake attempts at environmental reform?

Nations will not cooperate unless it is seen to be to their advantage to do so. As Archbishop William Temple once wrote: 'It may be the function of the Church to lead people to a purely disinterested virtue (although this is at least debatable); a statesman who believes that a mass of citizens can be governed without appeal to self-interest is living in dreamland and is a public menace. The art of government in fact is the art of so ordering life that self-interest prompts what justice demands.' What applies nationally to the mass of a nation's citizens applies equally on a global scale to all the nations of the world. Justice to future generations demands that the planet is not environmentally damaged; but it is unlikely that many policies to this end will be put into practice unless the governments of the countries of the world perceive that it is in their interests to do so. How can this be done? Appeals to retain the beauty of nature or to stop urbanization spoiling the look of the countryside are likely to fall on deaf ears. Statesmen need to be convinced that the health and well-being of their own people will be damaged unless steps are taken forthwith to clean up the environment and to enable it to regain its health. Statesmen will not be likely to act in this matter simply on conviction. They will need the consent and the prompting of the peoples whom they govern.

It follows, therefore, there is a great need for education about the environment not merely at government level, but also in the popular media; and pressure needs to be put on politicians to make changes. Young people are likely to respond more easily than the middle-aged, because the young are not always so materially minded, and young people will still be alive to suffer the disadvantages that environmentalists assure us lie in the future. One of the problems of environmental politics is that politicians and those who elect them are usually only concerned about short-term issues. But so far as the environment is concerned, damage done now usually does not show itself until a few years have passed.

Attitudes have already changed greatly. In the 1960s any who interested themselves in the environment were regarded as oddities and dismissed as 'eco-freaks'. But in 1972 the United Nations Conference on the Environment in Stockholm, preceded by René Dubois and Barbara Ward's bestselling book *Only One Earth*, changed that. It made a huge impression on public opinion worldwide. Just before the Gulf War, opinion polls in the UK showed the environment to be people's major concern. In 1990 52 per cent said that the environment would affect the way they voted, and 58 per cent said they would prefer to live in a country which emphasizes the environment more than living standards. But such support is fickle. During the recent recession support fell away. It was still strongest among young people. The bulk of the people need to be persuaded once again to support environmental policies.

There have been some remarkable examples of international cooperation; for example the Montreal Convention on the ozone layer, and the subsequent amendments to the convention. The majority of countries promised to phase out ozone depleting gases. But promises are not always kept. The industrialized countries said that they would provide £240 million to help poorer countries with new technology needed for the phase-out. Not all that sum has yet been provided. In 1979, at the United Nations Conference on Science and Technology, the richer countries similarly promised £250 million which has not all been given.

Yet slowly matters do progress. The European Community has pledged to stabilize carbon dioxide levels at 1990 levels by the year 2000. It has also issued directives about sulphur and nitrogen gases, so as to slow down the depredations of acid rain.

In 1992 a second United Nations conference on the Environment was held at Rio de Janeiro. Although inevitably there is a great deal of 'politicking' at these huge conferences, they have the benefit of publicizing environmental needs through the mass media. Not all the proposals at the Rio conference were agreed. But 'Agenda 21' which set out a long list of targets and schedules for solving particular problems has borne fruit even in the borough councils of Britain. A consultative process is in train in which it is intended that ordinary people should be involved. There was also an agreement on the protection of biodiversity. Unfortunately the USA did not agree to proposals for reducing carbon dioxide pollution. But steps forward, however tentatively, were made on this and other matters. Unfortunately action is needed urgently, and big changes in public attitudes and in governmental policies are required quickly if the planet is to be set on a really safe course.

The countries in the Two-Thirds World inevitably feel that the industrialized countries, which have caused most of the pollution, now want to stop the developing countries from doing what industrialized countries have been doing with impunity in the past. Until they can see that it is in their own interests to introduce environmentally friendly policies full success is difficult. There is the problem of a highly centralized and nationalistic China, with one fifth of the world's population, which has a phenomenal rate of industrial growth, and which has stated its aim of a refrigerator in every home. Others are naturally worried about the effect of this on the ozone layer. Such setbacks however must not obscure the fact that great progress has been made internationally in the last half century.

Help is coming from unexpected quarters. Mass communications, the internet and satellite television are bringing the world together as never before. It is therefore easier today than it ever has been to realize that we are all one world, that we are all kinsmen, that God made of one all the nations of mankind to dwell on the face of the earth, and that we must all sink or swim together.

Acts 17:22–28

Paul, standing in the middle of the Areopagus, said: 'Men of Athens, I perceive that in every way you are very religious. For as I passed along, and observed the objects of your worship, I found also an altar with this inscription, "To an unknown god." What therefore you worship as unknown, this I proclaim to you. The God who made the world and everything in it, being Lord of heaven and earth, does not live in shrines made by man, nor is he served by human hands, as though he needed anything, since he himself gives to all men life and breath and everything. And he made from one every nation of men to live on all the face of the earth, having determined allotted periods and the boundaries of their habitation, that they should seek God, in the hope that they might feel after him and find him. Yet he is not far from each one of us, for "In him we live and move and have our being", as even some of your poets have said, "For we are indeed his offspring."'

Comment on the reading

This is the first half of Paul's famous speech to the Athenians on Mars Hill. He adapted his message to people whom he was addressing. The Athenians were well-known for their philosophical inclinations. It was unusual for Paul, to judge from his extant letters and from the Acts of the Apostles, to write about our natural knowledge of God. He preferred to speak about revealed religion. But here he speaks to the Athenians in the kind of language that Athenians used. This part of his speech is typical of the kind of way that Jews would have defended their faith to the pagan world of their day. Paul fully admitted that there is in pagans some knowledge of God; but it is an ignorant and tentative kind of knowledge, while Paul can proclaim a definite and informed gospel.

There were many temples in the streets of the ancient

Greek world, as a walk around the excavated buildings along the main street of ancient Ephesus testifies. As he made his way to the Areopagus in Athens Paul had spied one dedicated to 'an unknown god'. This gave him the opportunity of making God better known. He shared the faith of the ancient world that the world was created by God, and that God is the author of everything in it. But God, he said, did not live in the many shrines which could be seen in all Greek cities. He is transcendent over everything, being Lord of heaven and earth. He is not in need of food offered in sacrifice upon the altars of pagan temples. He does not need anything because he created all things. He made human hands, so he does not need hand-service, but the worship of the human heart. All life comes from God: he breathes life into human bodies. The various races of mankind and the boundaries within which they live and the age in which they flourish are all under the providence of God.

Paul cited a pagan author (probably Aratus) to show that he was still on common ground with them. God, he said, had created the whole human race from one person, Adam. So the whole human race is united in one family. His spirit is in everyone, because God is not only transcendent over us: he is also immanent in us. Because he created the human race, we are his children; and if we are his children, it follows that we are all brothers and sisters.

A prayer of confession

We have squandered the gift of life.
The good life of some is built upon the pain of many;
the pleasure of a few on the agony of millions.
To you we lift our outspread hands.
We thirst for you in a thirsty land.
We worship death in our quest to possess ever more things;
we worship death in our hankering after our own security,

our own survival, our own peace,
as if life were divisible,
as if love were divisible,
as if Christ had not died for us.
To you we lift our outspread hands.

Prayer used at the sixth assembly of the World Council of Churches, Vancouver, 1983

A prayer

O God, you have made of one blood all nations of men and women who dwell on the face of the earth. Help all the nations to cooperate for the common good, and to work together to conserve the world in which we live.

20

The Church's role

Why should the Church be involved with environmental matters? In the first place it is God's world, and we are harming it, and the Church should have a particular concern for conserving the gifts that God has given us in our world.

God's creation should be respected. We may use it for our good; but we may not abuse it. In the past some people thought that the whole world was fallen, and that it was so evil that it didn't matter how much mankind abused it. That is a false idea. The environment is part of God's kingdom, and we must work with the natural laws which keep the environment comfortable for life.

Most Christians would admit that there is a problem, but not many seem prepared to do anything practical about the environment. The Church should be in the vanguard of the environmental movement. Instead it is lukewarm. It may pay lip service to it, but on the whole it does nothing, and does not even advise its congregations to be environmentally minded.

In the past the churches have encouraged actions that can now be seen to harm the environment, so that it has actually been accused of responsibility for its overexploitation. But in those days there was no great harm that could be done globally, because of the comparatively small numbers of people and our limited ability to exploit the environment. Today the situation has entirely changed.

It must be said that there have been some attempts by churches to arouse concern for the environment. In 1990 the

World Council of Churches staged a World Convocation on Justice, Peace and the Integrity of Creation in Seoul (but the Roman Catholic Church refused an invitation to join it). Earlier, in 1979 it had held a large conference in Boston, Massachusetts, on 'Faith, Science and the Future'. The World Council also held a hearing on nuclear power in Sigtuna, Sweden.

None of these cut much ice, even with the parent churches. The British Council of Churches, now defunct, held a public hearing on the nuclear breeder reactor in 1977. The Church of England has produced two Reports which have been debated, one way back in the old Church Assembly, and the other nearly ten years ago in the General Synod. None of these meetings have had much effect. There is in Britain a Christian Ecology Link for Christians concerned with the environment, but it does not have many members or much influence; and a group of evangelicals is presently attempting to rally concern in the Church.

Why has the Church given such little thought to the environment? There are several reasons. In the first place, many Christian people feel that they know too little about what is a technical subject. There will always be some experts who disagree; and there have been disagreements over such matters as the extent, if any, of global warming, or about the ability of the world to feed all its human inhabitants. Some people have said that with such disagreements among experts they cannot take up a particular position, because they lack expert knowledge. But that is not the case. There is a consensus both about global warming and about the potential of the world's cereal harvests. The 'precautionary principle' involves taking action before complete proof is forthcoming. The basic facts about the environment can easily be discovered by church men and women. Indeed they are recounted in this book.

A second reason for the Church's lukewarmness on environmental matters is due to a feeling that it should not be concerned with such mundane matters as rocks and air and temperatures. Its message is a spiritual gospel. To be concerned with the environment would mean that it was deserting its true vocation. When it should be preaching about salvation in Christ it would be involved with worldly matters. But Christianity involves faith not just in Christ, but in the triune God, Father, Son and Holy Spirit. The Blessed Trinity lies at the very heart of Christianity; and the Trinity involves faith in God the Creator, God the Redeemer and God the Sanctifier. Matters of creation are therefore of importance as well as matters of redemption.

A third reason is due to the Church's preoccupation with short-term social issues. Christians feel it is more important to be concerned with the welfare of people than the welfare of the environment. This is an understandable attitude, but it is mistaken, because the welfare of the environment affects the welfare of people. We are absolutely dependent on our environment for our well-bring.

Another reason for the Church's lukewarmness is a fear of diluting its message, and adopting the views of the 'New Age' movement. Many Christians are wary of aligning themselves with those whom they fear. This is an odd attitude. Christians normally cooperate with other people in aims that they have in common. It is unusual to ask someone about the nature of their fundamental beliefs before agreeing to work with them. If something needs to be done, then surely it would be more appropriate to welcome supporters, whatever they may believe, rather than to refuse to do it.

The real challenge of the environment today is that it requires fundamental changes in our attitudes if we are to cease to damage it. It also requires radical changes in our lifestyle.

It will further require far more cooperation between the developing and the developed world, to share out the earth's resources and to give help in technology transfers and in raising the level of education, for without women's education the disastrous increase in world population will not be stemmed. It is doubtful whether many Christians today are ready to take these radical steps. They are neither cold not hot: they are lukewarm. Yet they should be in the vanguard.

The Church itself should not enter into environmental politics. That is not its job. But its members should set an example in their local communities through their personal lifestyle.

Local church leaders should encourage and persuade their local authorities to be more environmentally minded, especially in connection with Agenda 21.

Christians should be active in national environmental voluntary agencies, and they should make use of their publications to keep themselves abreast of the changing situation.

The World Council of Churches, which is at present sponsoring a petition about global warming, could play a much more prominent part. It could even unite on common ground with members of other faiths to bring pressure on the international scene.

Above all, Christian leaders, both nationally and in dioceses (or church regions), should be much more active in keeping environmental issues in a high profile before the general public and in pointing out the vital moral and spiritual issues at stake. It is not the prophetic task of the Church to provide answers to political environmental questions. It is the task of the Church to insist, for the welfare of God's creation in the world, that these questions are urgently addressed, and that appropriate answers are found to them.

'God so loved the world that he gave his only Son, that whoever believes in him should not perish but have eternal life' (John 3:16). If God so loved the world, ought not Christians be active in conserving the world? If so, far more active witness is required from all Christians, from the bottom upwards and from the top downwards. That witness, at both ends, is at present tragically absent. May God grant that we shall get our priorities right!

Revelation 3:14–22

'And to the angel of the church in Laodicea write: "The words of the Amen, the faithful and true witness, the beginning of God's creation. I know your works: you are neither cold nor hot. Would that you were cold or hot! So, because you are lukewarm, and neither cold nor hot, I will spew you out of my mouth. For you say, I am rich, I have prospered, and I need nothing; not knowing that you are wretched, pitiable, poor, blind, and naked. Therefore I counsel you to buy from me gold refined by fire, that you may be rich, and white garments to clothe you and to keep the shame of your nakedness from being seen, and salve to anoint your eyes, that you may see. Those whom I love, I reprove and chasten; so be zealous and repent. Behold, I stand at the door and knock; if any one hears my voice and opens the door, I will come in to him and eat with him, and he with me. He who conquers, I will grant him to sit with me on my throne, as I myself conquered and sat down with my Father on his throne. He who has an ear, let him hear what the Spirit says to the churches." '

Comment on the reading

Laodicea stood in the Lycus valley in Asia Minor, now in Turkey. Founded in the third century BC, it became an affluent town under the Roman Empire. It was a banking centre, famous for its textile industry and also for its medical school, and a well-known ingredient for eye salve was made there. It suffered an earthquake in AD60, but its civic pride was such that it refused aid from imperial sources to repair the damage. The words of the letter to the Laodiceans are said to be those of the 'Amen'. We think of this meaning 'so be it'; but the Hebrew word is derived from a root meaning 'strength', and so it probably refers to Christ as the firm foundation. Because Christ spoke truly of his heavenly Father, he was 'the faithful and true witness'. He is called 'the beginning of God's creation'. He is the 'first-born of all creation' (Colossians 1:15) because he was before creation.

The author of the book of Revelation was concerned with the progress of the gospel, and he must have known that the church in Laodicea took its character from that of the town in which it was situated. Its members were wealthy and had profited from the wealth of the city. Their involvement with the gospel was only lukewarm. They had not fallen away from the faith, but they did not seem to care much about it, and it did not make much difference to their lives. It is the same today with many churches in affluent areas. The congregation thinks that it is doing well, but it does not realize that spiritually speaking it is 'wretched, pitiable, poor, blind and naked', and the author of the letter, under the inspiration of the Spirit, advises it to take urgent steps to put things right. The reference to eye salve no doubt is prompted by the 'Phrygian powder' produced in Laodicea for eye salve.

The threat is given that the church will be disowned by Christ. If Laodicean Christians are to survive they must recognize their true state, and open the door to Christ, who is the true source of spiritual wealth and vision. Christ will strengthen them by his sacrament of the Eucharist. The reference to Christ supping with them has eucharistic overtones.

The author of Revelation sees with a clear vision the extreme danger of lukewarmness in religion. They need to buy 'gold refined by the fire' to restore their earlier enthusiasm. They need white garments to hide from sight the shame of their nakedness. They are wretched, poor, pitiable, blind. Do you think that these words apply to Christians who are lukewarm about the welfare of God's creation? It is a world which God loves, and so we ought with especial care to listen to what the Spirit says to the churches over these matters of the environment.

A final prayer

O Lord, fill us with new hope for our future. Give us a new heart and will to work for the well-being of all. Open our eyes afresh to the glory of your grace in the world of nature, and help us to prepare for the coming of your kingdom. Make us to feel and know that all things are possible to us with the help of your grace, so that we may work with fresh zeal and real expectation to set right the health of the planet which you have given us for our habitation.

21

An environmental Ten Commandments

In 1971 I suggested an 'environmental Ten Commandments', not of course to supersede the biblical Commandments, but to supplement them. I reprint them here because they are even more relevant today.

I am the Lord your God: you shall have no other gods but me.

You shall not make to yourselves any graven image or idol, such as GNP or possessions or riches, whether in the heavens above or in the earth beneath or in the waters under the earth.

You shall not take the name of the Lord your God in vain by calling on his name but ignoring his spiritual law.

Remember that you set apart one day in the week for true festivity, or you will be bored stiff in the technological age you are bringing upon yourselves.

Honour your father and mother but do not seek to prolong their natural term of life so that they are miserable.

You shall not murder future generations by your present greed.

You shall not commit sexual sin by producing more children than is your right.

You shall not steal the inheritance of posterity.

You shall not bear false witness against your overseas neighbours by lying to yourself about the extent of their need.

You shall not covet an ever increasing standard of living.

Author's note

I first had the idea of Bible readings about the environment after a meeting called in the Diocese of Southwark to discuss how we could encourage church people to become more involved with environmental issues. It has obviously not been possible to find Bible readings directly concerned with all the subjects under discussion, because these issues did not exist in biblical times, but I hope that each biblical passage studied will be seen to have an important moral or spiritual connection with the environmental issue under consideration.

In writing these twenty chapters I have drawn on an earlier book of sermons which I published under the title *Preaching for Our Planet* (Mowbray 1991). The Friends of the Earth (whose Trust I lately chaired) has also furnished me with valuable information; and I have also used the excellent pamphlets of the Worldwatch Institute in Washington. I am particularly indebted to three publications:

The State of the Environment, OECD, 1991

James Lovelock, *Gaia: The Practical Science of Planetary Medicine*, Gaia Books, 1991

Indicators of Sustainable Development for the United Kingdom, HMSO, 1996

The biblical passages are taken from the Revised Standard Version.

Hugh Montefiore

NOTES

NOTES

NOTES

NOTES

NOTES